Shape

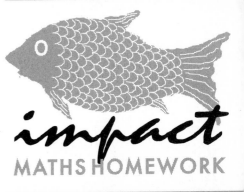

impact

MATHS HOMEWORK

Published by Scholastic Publications Ltd,
Villiers House,
Clarendon Avenue,
Leamington Spa,
Warwickshire CV32 5PR

© **1994 Scholastic Publications Ltd**
Text © **1994 University of North**
London Enterprises Ltd

UNIVERSITY OF
NORTH LONDON

Activities by the IMPACT Project
at the University of North
London, collated and rewritten
by Ruth Merttens and Ros Leather

Editor Jo Saxelby-Jennings
Assistant editor Joanne Boden
Designer Lucy Smith
Series designer Anna Oliwa
Illustrations James Alexander
Cover illustration Anna Oliwa

Designed using Aldus Pagemaker
Processed by Pages Bureau, Leamington Spa
Artwork by Pages Bureau, Leamington Spa
Printed in England by Clays Ltd, St Ives plc

British Library Cataloguing-in-Publication Data
A catalogue record for this book is
available from the British Library.

ISBN 0-590-53331-2

Shape

CONTENTS

Shape

impact
CONTENTS

impact
INTRODUCTION

This series of IMPACT books is designed to help you run a non-traditional homework scheme. Through the use of take-home maths activities, children can share maths with a parent/carer in the context of the home. The results of these activities then feed back into the classwork at school.

IMPACT works through the following processes:
● Teachers plan their maths for the next few weeks as usual and consider which parts might usefully be done at home.
● Teachers look through selected activities which fit in with what they are planning.
● The activities are photocopied and sent home with the children every week or fortnight.
● The results of each activity are brought back into the classroom by the children and form part of the following week's classwork.

In practice this process will be slightly different in each classroom and in each school. Teachers may adapt it to fit their own way of working and the ethos of the school in which they work. Most schools send out IMPACT activities fortnightly, although some do send it weekly. There is some evidence to suggest that weekly activities get a slightly better response and help to raise standards more effectively than fortnightly, but this is not conclusive. The important point is that

Planning

When you, the teacher, are looking at your work and deciding what maths, roughly speaking, you plan to be doing over the next few weeks, all that is necessary is to consider which parts may usefully be done or practised at home. It is helpful if, over a period of time, a range of activities are chosen in order to vary the mathematical experience in the home and the type and amount of follow-up required in class.

The activities tend to fall into three broad categories:
● Activities which practise a skill – these can be followed up in the routine classwork the children are doing. They must be carefully selected by the teacher according to the level of the children.
● Activities which collect data – these lead into work on data handling and representation.
● Activities in which children measure or make something – this produces an object or some measurements to be used later in class.

The activities in this book are divided into three sections according to age: Reception, Year 1 and Year 2. There are two pages of teachers' notes relating to the individual activities at the beginning of each section. All the activities are covered by the National Curriculum Attainment Target 'Shape, space and measures'. In general, the level of the activities is appropriate to the year of the child. Thus, Level 1 for Reception, Level 2 for Year 1 and Levels 2 and 3 for Year 2. Since the activities will be done by a child with an adult, in the context of the home, they are slightly more demanding in terms of level than would normally be the case

for shape activities in the classroom. Details of the relationships of the national curricula in Britain are given on page 96.

Working with parents

It is important for the success of IMPACT that the activities taken home are seen by the parents to be maths. We always suggest, at least until IMPACT is up and running and parents' confidence in it is well established, that activities are chosen which have a clearly mathematical purpose. Save the more 'wacky' activities until later! You will get a much better response if parents believe that what they are doing is maths.

Each activity contains a note to parents which explains the purpose of the activity and how they can best help. It also gives a reference to the attainment targets – although not to any level. Teachers who prefer not to have this can white it out. The IMPACT activities should be accompanied by an IMPACT diary, enabling parents and children to make their comments. See page 96 for details.

Making the most of IMPACT

The quickest way to reduce the number of children who share the maths at home is to ignore or be negative about the work they bring back into school. When the children come running into class, tripping over the string which went twice round their cat, it is difficult to welcome them all individually, but it is crucial that the activities are followed up in classwork. The nature and type of this follow-up depends very much upon the nature of the activity, and specific suggestions are made in the teachers' notes. However, some general points apply:
● Number activities, such as games, can often be repeated in a more formalised way in the classwork. For example, if the children have been playing a dice game,

throwing two dice and adding the totals, they can continue to do this in the classroom, but this time they can record all the 'sums' in their maths book. This applies to any skills-practice activity.
● Data-collecting activities, of any description, need to be followed up by allowing the children to work together in small groups to collate, analyse and represent their joint data. This will inevitably involve discussion as to how the data was obtained and any problems encountered while obtaining it.
● If the children have made or measured something at home, the information or the object needs to be used as part of the resulting classwork. This will not be too difficult since this type of activity is selected by the teacher precisely in order to provide the measurements or shapes for use in class.

The implication of this is that it is wise to select a variety of activities to send home. No teacher wants to drown in data, nor do they want all the IMPACT activities to result in more routine number work. Some activities generate lots of follow-up work while others require minimal follow-up – perhaps just a discussion about who won or lost, and how many times they played the game.

Many of the activities can lead to an attractive display or enable the teacher to make a class book. Such a book does not have to be 'grand'. It can be simply five or six large sheets of sugar paper folded in the middle and stitched/stapled with the children's work mounted inside it. The children love these books, and they make a fine record of their work. An IMPACT display board in the school entrance hall gives parents a sense that their work at home is appreciated.

For further details of IMPACT see page 96.

Teachers' notes
RECEPTION

Susie Shape The Susie pictures could be made into mobiles or used for a border to surround other shape pictures. The children may like to make shape pictures using different shapes. Encourage them to say how many of each shape they have in their pictures. Encourage the children to look for the shapes which are not the 'usual' way up, for example, squares standing on their corners and so on. Some children think that only equilateral triangles with the apex facing up are triangles. Talk about oblongs and squares. Remember that both oblongs and squares are rectangles.

A hat for teddy The children can order their conical hats from tallest to shortest or widest to narrowest. Those shorter or taller than three bricks can be put in sets, as could those narrower or wider, at the base, than a piece of string three bricks long. Make other circular shapes, such as cylinders. Talk about whether a cylinder or a cone will hold more if they are the same height. Find out by making them and filling them with lentils or rice.

Cones can be made into mice and displayed to illustrate a story about mice, such as Graham Oakley's *Church Mice* series (Macmillan Children's Books).

Fat mouse, thin mouse The children may like to create other models using this method, for example a Father Christmas or a clown's hat.

This is an ideal opportunity to study other shapes that taper to a point (that is, pyramids) whatever the shape of the base. Polydron (a construction kit consisting of flat plastic shapes which can be snapped together) is excellent for making pyramids. Children are fascinated by the names of these models, for example square-based pyramid.

Circles, circles Ask the children to choose their favourite circle to place in front of them and then all put their circles in order. Often, when positioning the circles, it is helpful if the children who think their circle is next, put their hand up. This ensures that each child has a turn. Ask them to all sit behind their circles and then ask questions such as, 'How many circles are bigger and how many are smaller than (say) Stuart's?' Make another shape in lots of different sizes, for example, a square or an oblong. What is the biggest square you can make? What is the smallest oblong?

Laying bricks You may be fortunate enough to have a parent who could come into school to demonstrate their bricklaying skills. The children could be engaged in cement-mixing and laying bricks in a variety of patterns. In any event, encourage the children to build a LEGO wall. Talk about the way that the bricks overlap. What other shapes can be used as bricks to make a wall? Discuss why circles don't make a good wall. How about squares or triangles (one apex up, and then one apex

down, and so on)? Draw some interesting walls and discuss them with the children.

Moving a load If you have some large cardboard cylinders and a board in school, the children can transport one another in this way. Please remind the children not to place their fingers near the edge of the board in case they become trapped. Would any shapes other than cylinders work under the board? How about spheres? Discuss the shapes of wheels. Look at lots of different sorts of wheels – ones with holes, with spokes or with solid centres. Which vehicles have the largest wheels and which have the smallest wheels? How many wheels do different vehicles have?

Building cuboid towers Perhaps a parent could come into school and demonstrate how a strong pillar is built using real bricks. The children may be allowed to experiment with the bricks and mortar to see how they are joined together. As an alternative modelling bricks, such as LEGO, could be used. Talk about different cuboids. A cube is a special sort of cuboid. What is special about it? Try building with cubes. Which are easier, brick shapes or cubes?

Walking a square This is an activity that children can enjoy in the hall or in the playground. Ask them to take turns in giving instructions. They may like to raise their right hand so that they all turn in the same direction. Once they are proficient, they may like to try walking round an obstacle while blindfolded, with another child giving instructions – this is very difficult!

Use all your containers Ask the children which shapes are the easiest and which are the most difficult for building with and why? Set the children challenges: limiting them to a few containers or only allowing them to use cylinders in their models and so on. Suppose they are allowed to use adhesive or sticky tape. Which shapes are difficult to stick and which are easy? Can the children explain why? Talk about faces, edges and corners. In order to stick something properly, you need at least one flat face.

Make a shape picture Give the children an opportunity to talk about their pictures. They may like to write down how many of the various shapes they used. Their work could then be displayed, naming the different shapes. For example, 'I have used two oblongs and three circles in my picture.' Discuss the fact that oblongs and squares are both rectangles. Talk about the differences between the shapes. How many sides do they have? What makes an oblong different from a square? Encourage the children to describe the differences.

In a pickle! The children could play the game 'Simon says' to make this activity more exciting. Please ensure that the instructions include the words 'right' and 'left'. The singing game 'Hokey-cokey' would also help the children to understand the difference between right and left. Any children who are having real difficulty remembering left and right can be helped by writing or sticking 'L' and 'R' on their hands. Alternatively, you can tie luggage labels on to their wrists or stick self-adhesive labels to their toes!

Potato prints The children could work in groups to make further printed patterns. Each group could decide on a favourite shape that it would like to use and the type of pattern; for example, a cat or rabbit and a quarter turn pattern. Their results could be displayed alongside a class book showing their homework. Encourage the children to count the number of prints they have made. Who has printed the most shapes and who has printed the least?

Initial shape Display the children's drawings of their initials and talk about the shapes. Which letters have circles or parts of circles? Which have triangles? Which have squares or parts of squares? Design some new shapes (for example, ⬭) and let the children use these to create letters. Try the same thing using numerals. Which numerals have straight lines and which have curly lines? How many numerals have both straight and curly lines?

My favourite solid shape Perhaps the children can be encouraged to make their three-dimensional shapes in class. If you have any parents who are willing to help in the classroom, this is an ideal activity for them to share. The children can use anything – nets (some simple ones are given in the back of this book on pages 94 and 95), Polydron or similar construction kits, Multilink, Plasticine, Playdoh and so on.

Portrait shapes Mount all the portraits, giving the children the chance to 'improve' them in class if they were done a bit hurriedly at home. Then make a portrait gallery of all their pictures arranged according to shape – all the squares

together, all the ovals together and so on. Talk about the names of the different shapes. Does it make any difference which way up they are? Talk about the different shapes they have chosen for their frames. What are the various shapes called – 'oblong', 'square', 'circle', 'oval', 'triangle' and so on. Talk about the fact that both squares and oblongs are rectangles.

Family favourite! The children can cut out their drawings of shapes and sort them into coloured hoops. For example, all the three-sided shapes in the yellow hoop, all the four-sided shapes in the green hoop, all those with curved sides in the red hoop and so on. The children can discuss how they can sort the shapes. Can they name any of the shapes?

Where is it? The children can play the game in class, as a group game 'on the rug', where one or two children place the LEGO bricks and the rest of the class guess where they are. This game can lead into 'Kim's game', where several things are positioned on a tray and the children have to shut their eyes while one is removed. Use positional words to describe which one was removed. It helps if all the objects on the tray are of the same type; for example, all bricks, as then they are likely to be identified by reference to position.

Window watch The children can make a display of all their windows and the views through them. Talk about the different shapes. How many straight sides do they have? Which shapes have curved sides? Display them under the name of the shape. Children like names such as 'hexagon' and 'pentagon' for six-sided and five-sided

shapes. (Remember that any six-sided shape is a hexagon and any five-sided shape is a pentagon and so on.)

Home match When the children bring in their drawings, discuss them. Have any of the children drawn the same examples? For example, the TV for the cube or tins of food for the cylinder? Mount all their drawings and display them in appropriately labelled sets on the wall – cylinders, cubes, cuboids and spheres. Discuss how we might try to make a cube, cuboid or cylinder out of paper – this will lead on to 'nets'.

Triangle search The children can draw different types of triangle in class. Can they each draw a different triangle, colour it in and cut it out, and then make pictures by combining several children's triangles? Some triangles 'lean backwards', some are 'upside-down', but they are all three-sided. Extend the activity by looking at four-sided shapes. Draw some unusual four-sided shapes. Talk about squares and oblongs. What is special about them (that is, they have four right angles)? Remind the children that they are both types of rectangle.

Rectangle search In class, the children can draw different types of rectangle. Can they each draw a different rectangle, colour it in and cut it out, and then make pictures by combining several children's rectangles? Some rectangles are square, some are 'thin' oblongs and some are 'fat' oblongs, but they are all four-sided with four right angles. Remember that a square is a type of rectangle!

Square patterns How many different patterns have the children created when making their squares? What fraction of each square has been coloured? The children can create square, symmetrical, patchwork pictures using some of the patterns. Can they calculate how many more squares and what patterns are needed to make their designs symmetrical? Extend the activity by using a different shape, such as an oblong. Can they make oblong shapes in the same way? Remind them that the shapes achieved by drawing in the diagonals are still triangles!

_____and
child

_____
helper(s)

_____
did this activity together

Susie Shape

- Carefully colour these shapes and cut them out.

- Stick them together on another piece of paper to make Susie Shape.

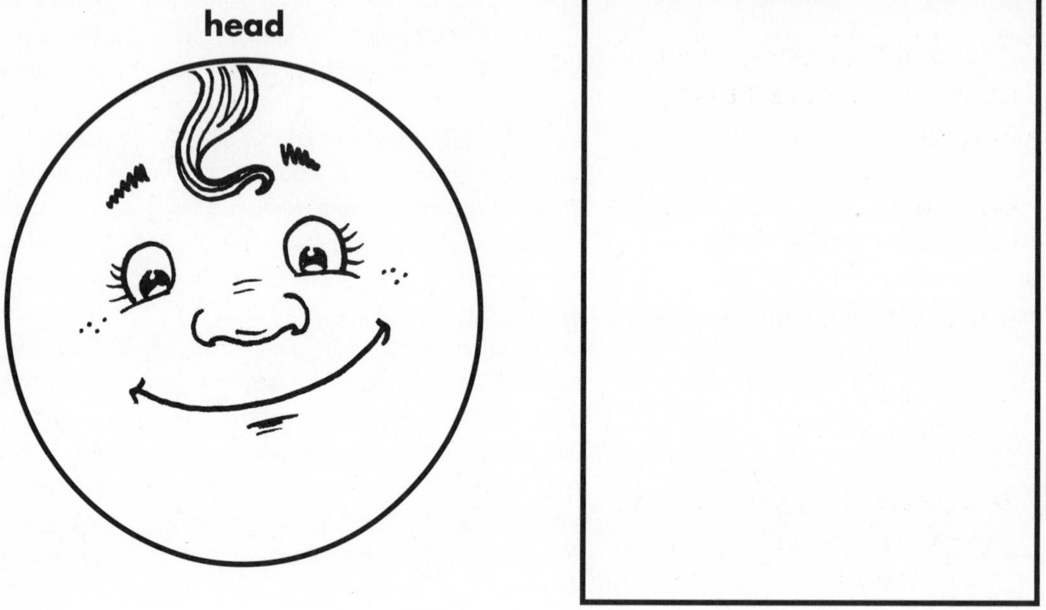

head

body

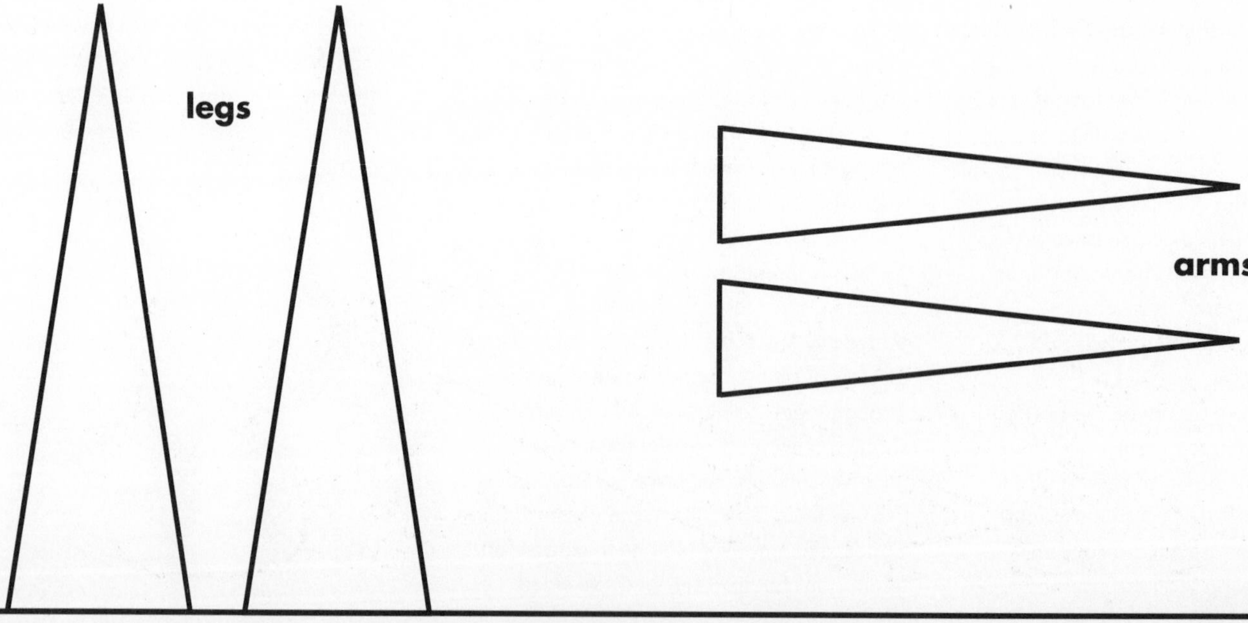

legs

arms

impact MATHS HOMEWORK

A hat for teddy

YOU WILL NEED: a sheet of paper, some sticky tape and a mug or saucer.

● Draw round a saucer or mug to make a circle shape.

● Cut out your circle.

● Fold your circle in half and cut it along the fold.

● Stick the two straight edges of one of your semicircles together. You will now have a cone-shaped hat for teddy.

Dear Parent or Carer

Your child may like to experiment by making different-sized cones. If a smaller segment is cut out of the circle used to make the hat, you will get a flatter cone. You may like to talk about ice-cream cones and clowns' hats. Your child may like to decorate the hat.

National Curriculum reference:
Maths Attainment Target
Shape, space and measures

_____and

child

_____

helper(s)

_____

did this activity together

impact MATHS HOMEWORK

_____and
child

_____
helper(s)

_____
did this activity together

Fat mouse, thin mouse

YOU WILL NEED: a circle of paper and some sticky tape.

● To make the paper circle, draw round a mug or saucer and cut out the shape.

● Fold your circle in half and cut along the fold.

● Stick the two straight sides of one of the semicircles together.

● Draw round a 2p coin, cut out the circle and fold it in half. Do this again. These circles will make the mouse's ears.

● Use a 1p coin to draw round for the eyes.

● Cut long strips of paper to attach for the whiskers and the tail.

● Do you think that your mouse is fat or thin? When you have decided, use another circle to make a fatter or thinner mouse.

Circles, circles

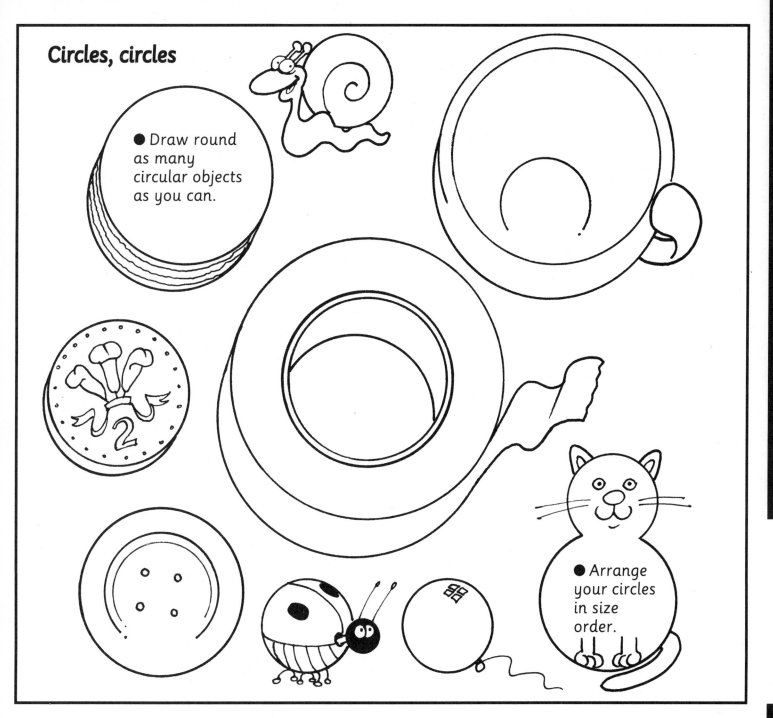

● Draw round as many circular objects as you can.

● Arrange your circles in size order.

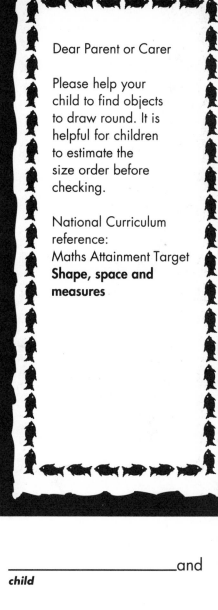

Dear Parent or Carer

Please help your child to find objects to draw round. It is helpful for children to estimate the size order before checking.

National Curriculum reference:
Maths Attainment Target
Shape, space and measures

_____and

child

_____

helper(s)

_____

did this activity together

_____and
child

_____
helper(s)

_____

did this activity together

Laying bricks

● Look at a brick wall to see how the bricks have been laid.

● Why do you think that the builder has laid the bricks in this way?

● Try making a brick wall with LEGO bricks.

impact MATHS HOMEWORK

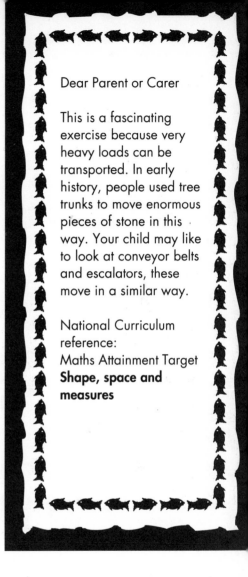

Dear Parent or Carer

This is a fascinating exercise because very heavy loads can be transported. In early history, people used tree trunks to move enormous pieces of stone in this way. Your child may like to look at conveyor belts and escalators, these move in a similar way.

National Curriculum reference:
Maths Attainment Target
Shape, space and measures

Moving a load

YOU WILL NEED: at least four cylindrical tins of about equal size, a chopping (or pastry) board and something quite heavy to move.

● Lay down the tins and put the board on top.

● Practise rolling the board over the tins.

● Once a tin has been uncovered, put it under the front of the board.

_____and
child

_____
helper(s)

_____
did this activity together

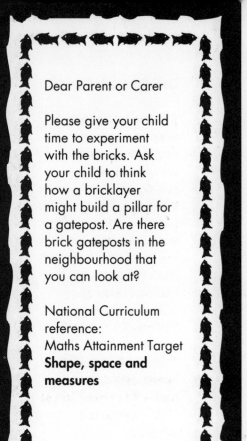

_____and

child

_____

helper(s)

_____

did this activity together

Building cuboid towers

YOU WILL NEED: several building bricks.

● Try building two towers using the bricks – use the bricks flat for one tower and upright for the other.

● Which tower is the easiest to build?

● Which tower is the most stable?

● Which tower uses the most and which the least bricks to reach the same height?

impact MATHS HOMEWORK

Walking a square

- Can you walk in a square shape?

- How many steps does each side have?

- How many corners?

- Draw the shape that you have made.

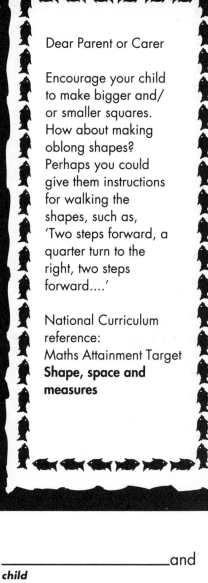

Dear Parent or Carer

Encourage your child to make bigger and/ or smaller squares. How about making oblong shapes? Perhaps you could give them instructions for walking the shapes, such as, 'Two steps forward, a quarter turn to the right, two steps forward....'

National Curriculum reference:
Maths Attainment Target
Shape, space and measures

_____and

child

_____

helper(s)

_____

did this activity together

_____and

child

_____

helper(s)

_____

did this activity together

Use all your containers

YOU WILL NEED: an assortment of solid containers.

● Can you build a model using all of your containers, but without using adhesive?

● Can you give someone else instructions for building a model using all of the containers?

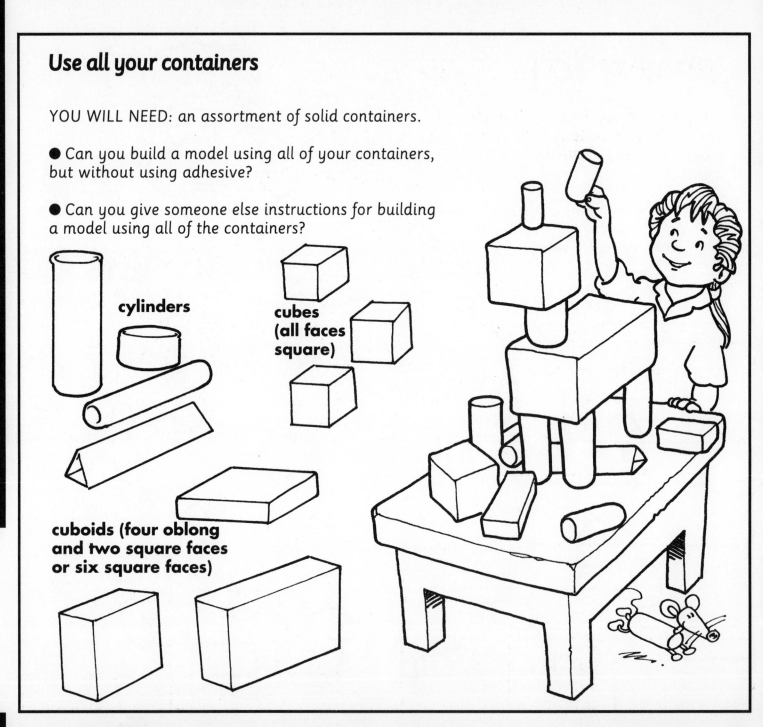

cylinders

cubes (all faces square)

cuboids (four oblong and two square faces or six square faces)

impact MATHS HOMEWORK

Make a shape picture

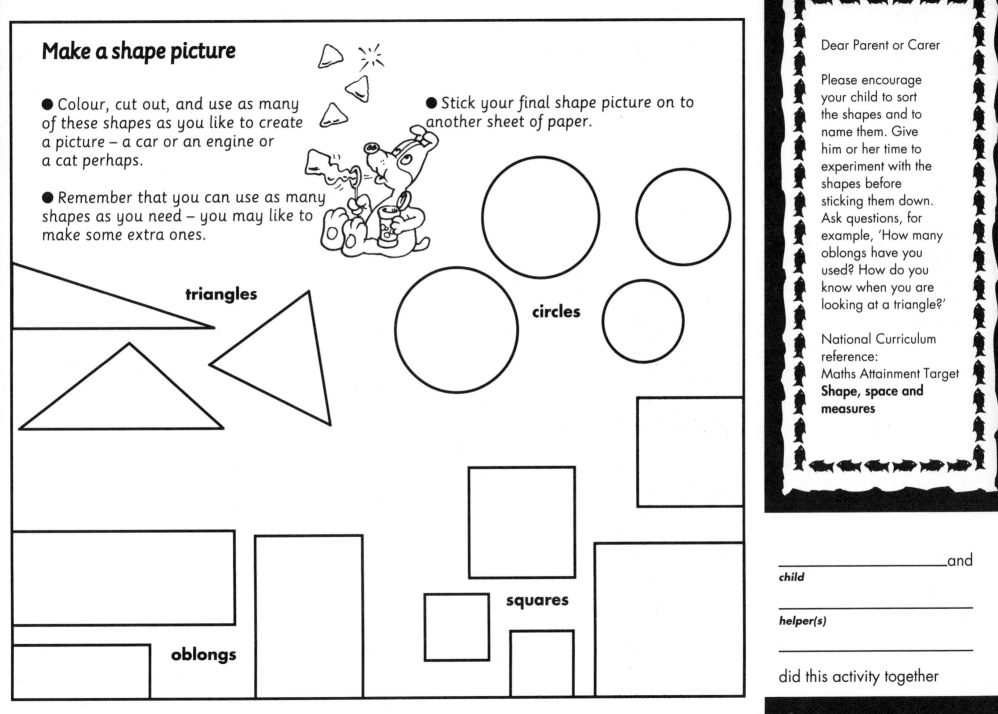

● Colour, cut out, and use as many of these shapes as you like to create a picture – a car or an engine or a cat perhaps.

● Remember that you can use as many shapes as you need – you may like to make some extra ones.

● Stick your final shape picture on to another sheet of paper.

triangles

circles

squares

oblongs

Dear Parent or Carer

Please encourage your child to sort the shapes and to name them. Give him or her time to experiment with the shapes before sticking them down. Ask questions, for example, 'How many oblongs have you used? How do you know when you are looking at a triangle?'

National Curriculum reference:
Maths Attainment Target
Shape, space and measures

_____and

child

_____

helper(s)

_____

did this activity together

_____and

child

_____

helper(s)

_____

did this activity together

In a pickle!

YOU WILL NEED: four large circles of card – made from old cereal boxes, one red, one blue, one green and one yellow – the instruction cards drawn opposite and a box or bag.

● Place the coloured circles fairly close together on the floor in a square pattern. They must not be moved during the game.

● Cut out the instruction cards and put them in the box.

● Each time your partner takes an instruction card out of the box and reads it out, you must follow that instruction.

● Tell them to replace the card after reading it.

● How many instructions can you follow before you get 'in a pickle!'?

● How many can your partner follow?

right foot → yellow	left foot → yellow	right foot → green	left foot → green
right hand → yellow	left hand → yellow	right hand → green	left hand → green
right foot → blue	left foot → blue	right foot → red	left foot → red
right hand → blue	left hand → blue	right hand → red	left hand → red

impact MATHS HOMEWORK

Potato prints

YOU WILL NEED to make a potato print of the first letter of your name, first name or surname, with some paint and a potato. Ask an adult to help you cut the potato.

● Dip your potato into some paint and print it on to some paper.

● Can you print these designs?

● What comes next?

● Can you make any other patterns? Bring them into school.

Dear Parent or Carer

Please help your child to make the potato print; your child could draw the letter shape for you to cut. Talk to your child about different ways of moving the letter, such as a quarter turn and a half turn or rotation.

National Curriculum reference:
Maths Attainment Target
Shape, space and measures

_____and

child

_____

helper(s)

_____

did this activity together

_____and

child

_____

helper(s)

_____

did this activity together

Initial shape

● Write your initials very large and clear on this page.

● What shapes can you see in them?

My favourite solid shape

- What is your favourite solid shape?

- Can you see it on this page?

- Is there anything in or around your home which is this shape? Can you draw it?

- Bring your drawings into school.

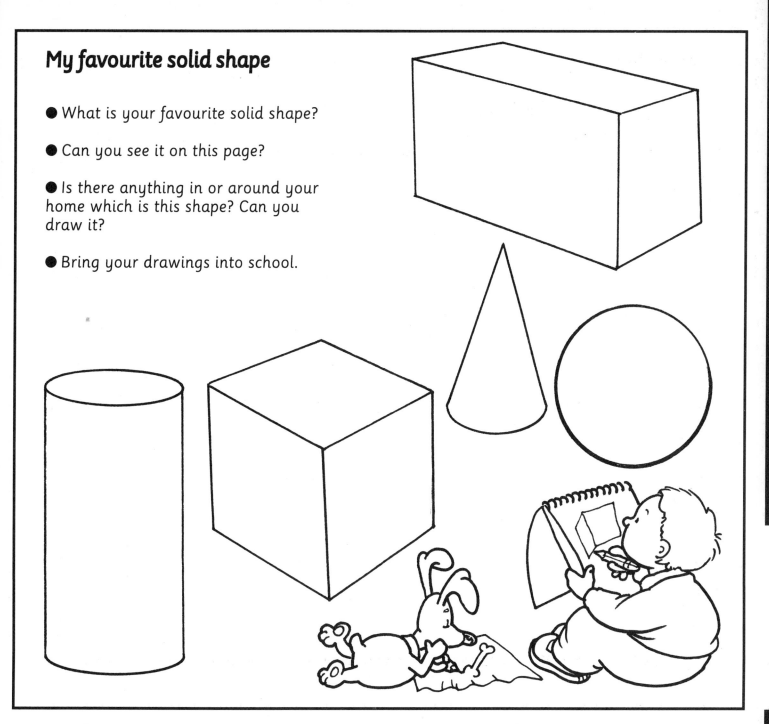

Dear Parent or Carer

Please discuss the different three-dimensional (that is, solid) shapes with your child. There are many different shapes, not drawn on this page, which they could select and draw! Your child may need some help with planning how to draw their shape.

National Curriculum reference:
Maths Attainment Target
Shape, space and measures

_____and

child

_____

helper(s)

_____

did this activity together

_____and

child

_____

helper(s)

_____

did this activity together

Portrait shapes

● Choose one of the shapes below and copy it into the space opposite.

● Now use your shape as a frame and draw a portrait in it of someone in your home. It could be a brother, friend, parent, granny, yourself, or even the cat!

● Bring your picture into school.

Family favourite!

● Ask each person in the family to draw their favourite shape below and colour it in beautifully.

● Which shape is your favourite?

● Bring all the drawings into school.

Dear Parent or Carer

Talk to your child about the different shapes. We are looking at different types of two-dimensional (that is, flat) shapes and we shall be discussing in class how they are classified.

National Curriculum reference:
Maths Attainment Target
Shape, space and measures

_____and

child

_____

helper(s)

_____

did this activity together

Where is it?

YOU WILL NEED: a mug and a pile of LEGO bricks.

● Take it in turns with someone to place a LEGO brick either **in, under, on top of** (turn the mug upside down) or **beside** the mug. The other person must turn their back so they can't see.

● Now your helper must guess which of these four positions they think you have chosen.

● If they are right, they get to keep the LEGO brick.

● Play again using another LEGO brick.

For example, suppose you place the LEGO brick in the mug, and your helper (who is not looking!) guesses, 'On top of.' Since the brick is not on top of the mug, she doesn't get to keep it.
  Now she puts the LEGO brick in, on, under or beside the mug and you guess.

● Keep playing until one of you has three LEGO bricks!

impact MATHS HOMEWORK

Window watch

- Make a window frame in your favourite shape from cardboard.

- Cut it out.

- Now draw something you might be able to see through it! Use the back of this sheet.

- Bring your drawing into school.

_____and

child

_____

helper(s)

_____

did this activity together

 **MATHS HOMEWORK**

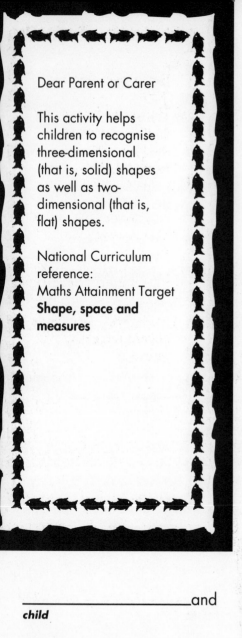
_____and
child

_____
helper(s)

_____
did this activity together

Home match

● Find these shapes around the home.

● Ask someone to help you draw and write the name of something which is the same shape as each one.

cube

sphere

cylinder

cuboid

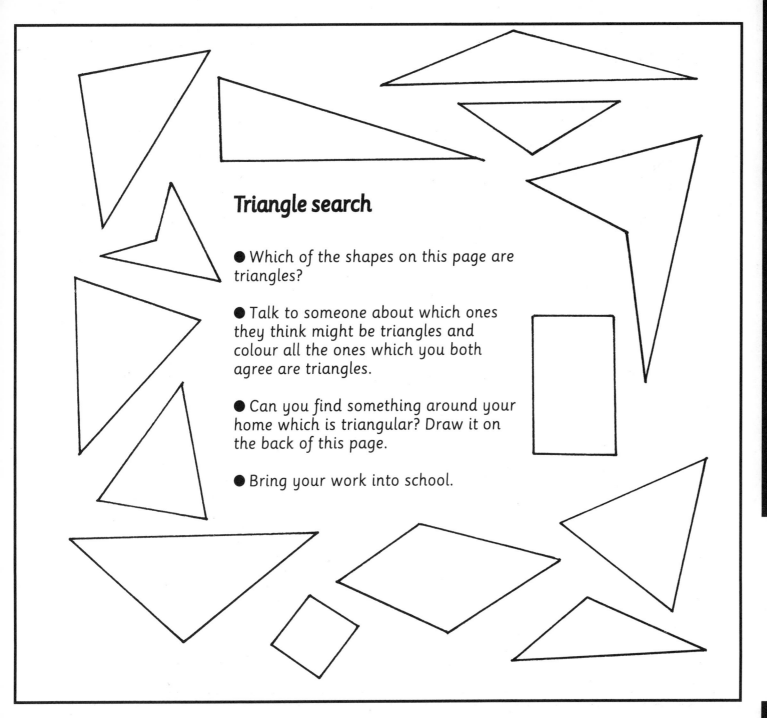

Triangle search

● Which of the shapes on this page are triangles?

● Talk to someone about which ones they think might be triangles and colour all the ones which you both agree are triangles.

● Can you find something around your home which is triangular? Draw it on the back of this page.

● Bring your work into school.

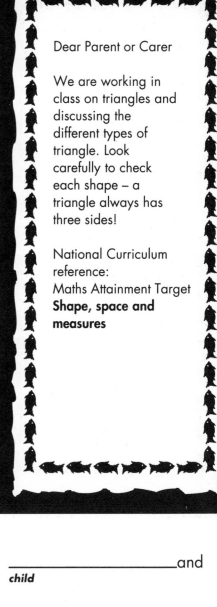

Dear Parent or Carer

We are working in class on triangles and discussing the different types of triangle. Look carefully to check each shape – a triangle always has three sides!

National Curriculum reference:
Maths Attainment Target
Shape, space and measures

_____and

child

_____

helper(s)

_____

did this activity together

Dear Parent or Carer

We are working in class on rectangles and discussing the different types of rectangle. Look carefully to check each shape – a rectangle always has four sides and four right angles. And remember, a square is a type of rectangle!

National Curriculum reference:
Maths Attainment Target
Shape, space and measures

_____and

child

_____

helper(s)

_____

did this activity together

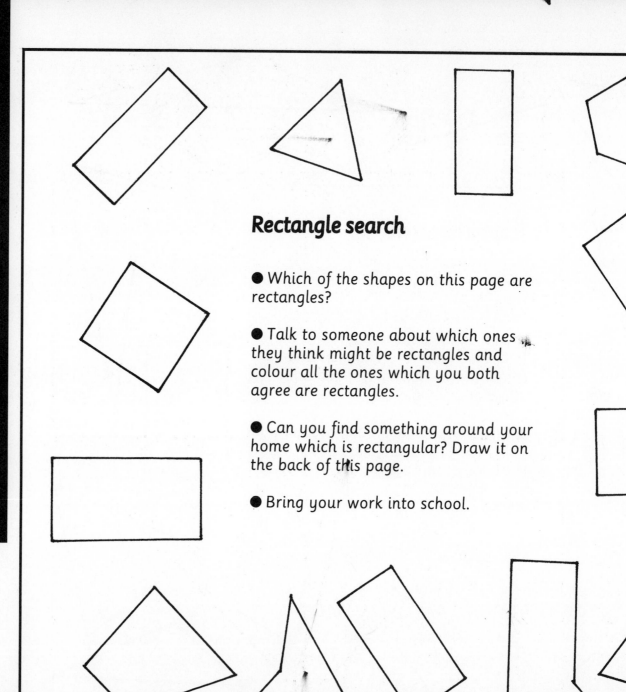

Rectangle search

● Which of the shapes on this page are rectangles?

● Talk to someone about which ones they think might be rectangles and colour all the ones which you both agree are rectangles.

● Can you find something around your home which is rectangular? Draw it on the back of this page.

● Bring your work into school.

Square patterns

● Colour the INSIDE square, using one colour only.

● Then cut out all the triangles contained in the OUTSIDE square.

● How many triangles are there?

● Rearrange your shapes into a new square pattern of the same size as the original.

● How many different square patterns can you make of this size?

● Stick your favourite square pattern on to a piece of paper to bring into school.

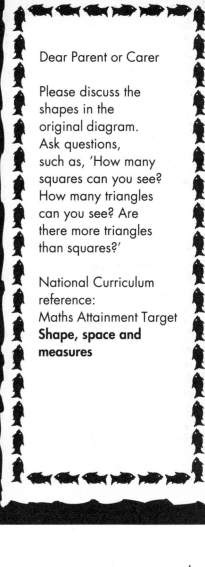

Dear Parent or Carer

Please discuss the shapes in the original diagram. Ask questions, such as, 'How many squares can you see? How many triangles can you see? Are there more triangles than squares?'

National Curriculum reference:
Maths Attainment Target
Shape, space and measures

_____and
child

_____
helper(s)

_____
did this activity toget

Shape

Teachers' notes
YEAR ONE

Patterned snake game The children could cut out their snakes and display them in a 'Snake book'. Has anyone created a snake similar either in pattern or in colour? How many different patterns are there? Talk about the differences between the shapes which they used on their snakes. How many sides does a square or a pentagon have? What do we call a shape with six sides? Encourage the children to articulate the differences between the shapes, both in terms of the numbers of sides they have and in terms of whether those sides are straight or curved.

Boxes, tins and balls In the classroom, you will need a supply of cuboids, cylinders and spheres in a variety of sizes and two large hoops. Then the children can justify their sorting. Perhaps they could choose some other ways of sorting the shapes. Ask each child to choose a solid shape. Let one child describe their shape and ask all those children who have that shape to hold it up. For example, 'This shape has a circle at the ... the bottom, it will roll and build.' ... deal time to discuss the ... es.

... The children may ... ers and put them

into sets, for example those that are taller or shorter than five bricks, or those that are fatter or thinner than a piece of string five bricks long. Can the children sit holding their cylinders in order of 'fatness'? Perhaps they could each say a sentence, '(So many) people have taller cylinders and (so many) people have shorter cylinders than mine.' Will the order be the same for longest to shortest as for fatness?

Walking round the table This is an excellent activity for PE time. The children can walk squares and rectangles. If you have a Valiant Roamer or Turtle your children can write programs for moving along a specified route. Talk about half and quarter turns. How many quarter turns make a complete circle? How many half turns make a complete circle? Can they turn half of a quarter turn?

A newspaper bridge The children will need to discuss how their bridges have been constructed. Did any of them make pillars to support their bridge? What shape are the pillars? Do all the bridges work? What was the most difficult part to construct? The children could build a bridge out of PE equipment and act out the story of *The Three Billy Goats Gruff*. Discuss the idea of suspension bridges. Can they make one of these in class? How much weight will it hold? How are they going to test it?

Three boxes You will need a selection of cuboid boxes. Ask each child to choose a box. Can they arrange themselves in order according to the height of their box? What about box width order? Who has the narrowest box? Can everyone find the depth of their box? What does the 'depth'

mean? Are there any boxes which are not cuboid? Talk about the fact that cubes are a special sort of cuboid. What makes a cube special? Are some boxes not cuboid at all? If possible, provide an example of a non-cuboid box (for example, a circular cheese spread container). Talk about what shape this is (cylindrical)?

Faces The children can sort their boxes using the face shapes to help them place the boxes in the correct set. Do all the cuboids have six rectangular faces? (Some may have two square faces and four rectangular faces.) Can the children use Polydron or a similar construction kit to recreate their boxes? Talk about the different shapes of the faces. Do any of the boxes have circular faces (as in some cheese spread boxes) or hexagonal faces (as in some chocolate boxes)? Which box do the children like best?

Right-angled foods The children can compare their foods! Which ones are exact right angles? Which ones have smaller, and which have larger, angles? The terms 'acute angle' (that is, smaller than 90°) and 'obtuse angle' (that is, larger than 90°) may be introduced – children quite like these terms! Talk about all the right angles you can see around your classroom and collect examples. The children can also look at body right angles. For example, they can make right angles with their elbows, or with their knees. What about with their waists?

Pentagon search The children can draw different types of pentagon in class. Can they each draw a different pentagon, colour it in and cut it out, and then make a picture by combining several children's

pentagons together? Some pentagons are regular (as in the Pentagon, the Washington HQ of the US defence forces), some are rocket-shaped, some are like houses, but they are all five-sided.

Hexagon search The children can draw different types of hexagon in class. Can they each draw a different hexagon, colour it in and cut it out, and then make a picture by combining several children's hexagons together? Some hexagons are regular (as in the honeycomb in a beehive), some are rocket-shaped, some are like arrows, but they are all six-sided.

Shape cost The children's pictures can be displayed. Can they work out how much it would cost to buy two or three of their pictures? Can they add in some new shapes? What are these called? How much would they be worth? How about a pentagon or an octagon? Remember that a hexagon, a pentagon or an octagon do not have to have sides of equal length! Make a class picture using lots of different shapes and add up the cost all together! Use real coins, if necessary.

Shape puzzle The children can discuss and compare their solutions. Were they all the same? They can play the same game, but on a four by four grid with an extra shape as well – a hexagon. This makes it much harder! Can they invent a similar game using numbers – that is three 1s, three 2s and three 3s. Those who have done the 3×3 shape game should find this easy. What does each row and each column add up to?

Building lines The children's drawings can be displayed – allowing time for any

Shape

impact MATHS HOMEWORK

improvements to their work to be made in class, if they feel they did it a bit hastily at home. Can they count the number of vertical lines they can see around the classroom? How many horizontal lines can they see? Of which are there more? Are there any lines on their drawings which are not horizontal or vertical? What do they call these? How do they describe them (for example, diagonal)?

Celtic crosses The crosses can all be mounted and displayed. They will make a beautiful display. Talk about the shapes the children have used. Which use curved lines? Which use straight lines? Can the children design a cross inside a circle? Can they create crosses using triangles? Talk about the different shapes used, for example, oblongs, triangles and circles. How many sides do they each have? Can they make another shape similar to a circle using only one line (for example, an oblong)?

Shape numbers The children can discuss which numbers they made and how. Some of these might make a nice display. The children could talk also about what each shape is called. Can they tell the difference between a square and an oblong? Which shapes have four sides? Which have only three? How many sides does a circle have?

Corner count-up The children can compare their drawings. Can they choose their favourite shapes and draw them big, colour them in and cut them out. These big shapes can then be displayed according to their numbers of corners. Count on each shape to show that the number of corners is the same as the number of sides. Talk about

the fact that some corners are right angles and some are not. Which shapes contain right angles? How many right angles do they each contain? For example, a triangle might contain one right angle, but it can not have two!

Curly and straight Display big numerals on the wall under the three headings in the table. Talk about straight and curly lines. Talk about how we draw the numerals – starting at the top. Display a picture of a small creature – a snail or a frog – at the top of each numeral to show the children where to begin when writing that number. This will help them as they write the numbers in their work.

Sandwiches Groups of children may like to make different mobiles, beginning with, for example, square shapes and demonstrating repeated halving. For example, a square could be followed by two rectangles, then four rectangles, then eight rectangles and so on. Children find it fascinating to see how folding doubles the number of shapes. Give them time to predict what will happen next.

Starry hexagons These stars make excellent decorations for festival displays. The children may like to investigate different ways of making stars using pentagons, two equilateral triangles or by folding and cutting squares. Look at the stars they make and talk about them. How many sides does each star have? Do they all have the same number of sides? What is it that characterises a star? Do they all have the same number of points and so on?

Bird's-eye view Groups of children could arrange themselves using different

criteria from their homework; for example, table shape, number of squares or circles on the table and so on. Different groups could be involved with drawing plans of tables for the Three Bears. What shaped tables could they have? In what order will the bears be seated? What shaped bowls will they choose? Their own table plans could be stuck in a book and displayed near their designs for the Three Bears.

Looking from above The children could display their bird's-eye views and have a 'Guess what it is?' competition. Why are some of the objects easier to identify than others? Can other views be drawn of the same objects to help with recognition? Can they draw some three-dimensional shapes looking down on them? How about a cube or a cuboid or a cylinder or a sphere? Which are easy and which are hard to draw?

My shape party hat Are the children able to arrange themselves in groups according to their chosen shape? What criteria will they choose? Can they cut and arrange sandwiches in their chosen shapes? Perhaps simple biscuits could be made into the required shapes and a real shape party organised. Talk about the flat shapes we can see on the faces of the three-dimensional shapes. How many faces does each three dimensional shape have? How many corners?

Make a jigsaw Encourage the children to extend their ideas by using a square piece of card and sticking an identical picture on each side (one of the pictures can be rotated through 90°). How long does it take to make this jigsaw? If these

jigsaws have been carefully produced, they could be sold as small gifts at the school fête.

Shape game This activity can be recreated using hoops. Can the children find, or design, shapes to fit each category? You could make up other categories. Which shapes can be named? Play a 'Guess which shape I'm describing' game. This will encourage the children to use precise, mathematical vocabulary.

Hexagons The children may like to read the story of *The Patchwork Quilt* (Penguin) by Valerie Flournoy. They can decorate their hexagonal shapes with a favourite pattern. Their shapes can be used to design a large, tessellating picture. What other shapes will tessellate? Can they think about tessellating four-sided shapes? What about triangles? Why do circles not tessellate? Also discuss the symmetry of each shape. Are all the hexagons given symmetrical? If they are not, will they tessellate?

Plasticine cubes How many different Plasticine shapes did the children discover? Can they name and describe each shape? If a cube is cut into quarters what shapes do they get? Are all the quarters the same shape? Can the quarters be rearranged to form a new three-dimensional shape? Encourage the children to experiment. They may make up names for their shapes, and this is fine. Introduce 'correct' mathematical terminology if you feel they will enjoy it and take it on board, for example, calling a pyramid a square-based pyramid or a tetrahedron (a triangular-based pyramid).

Patterned snake game

This is a game for two people.

YOU WILL NEED: a building brick, some crayons, a counter for each player and the playing board provided.

● Cut out the shapes opposite and stick them on to the faces (sides) of the building brick.

● Both players need to choose a snake and design a repeating pattern along it, using the same shapes as those on the brick, with one shape in each space on their snake. Do not use the 'Smiley' in your patterns.

● Colour in your snakes with care. Use the same colour for each shape; for example, colour all squares in red and all the triangles in blue.

● Put your counters on your snakes' heads.

● Take turns at throwing the brick. When the shape on the brick matches the next shape on your snake you can move your counter forward one shape.

● If you throw a 'Smiley' you can move forward one shape, whatever it is.

● The first person to move their counter to the end of their snake is the winner.

oblong

square

triangle

circle

Smiley

pentagon

Patterned snake game

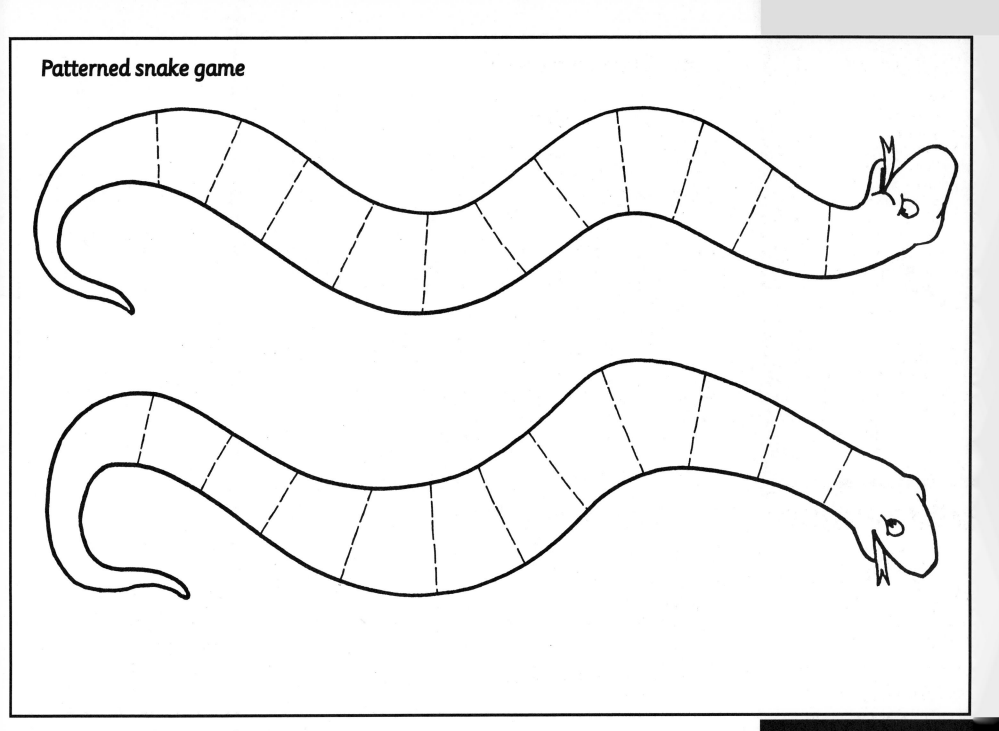

Boxes, tins and balls

YOU WILL NEED: several boxes (cuboids), tins (cylinders) and balls (spheres).

● Try each type of shape to see whether it will roll or build.

● Write the names or draw pictures of the shapes in the right sets.

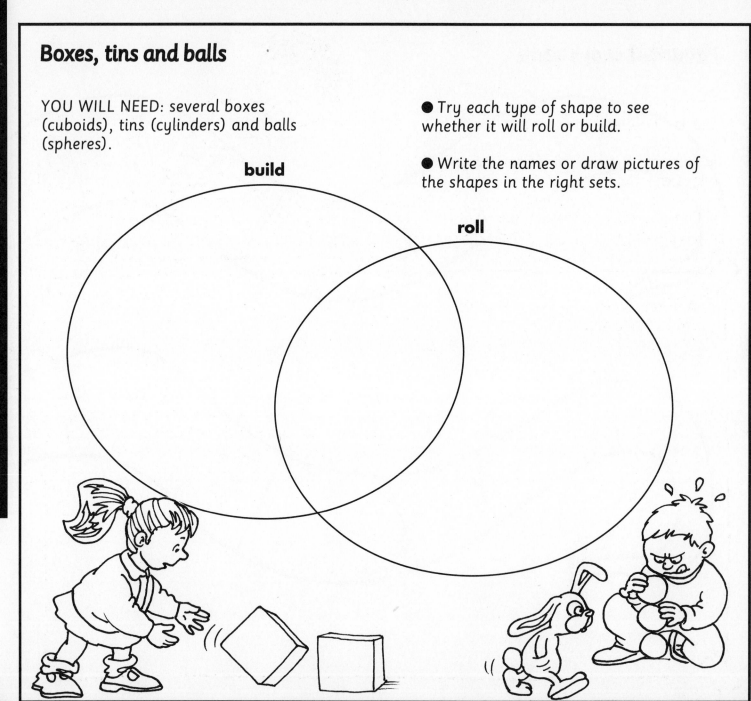

Fat and thin cylinders

YOU WILL NEED: two oblong-shaped sheets of paper and some sticky tape.

● Roll up a sheet of paper and stick the edges together.

● Can you make a fat cylinder and a thin cylinder from paper of the same size?

● In this space, draw two things which are cylinders.

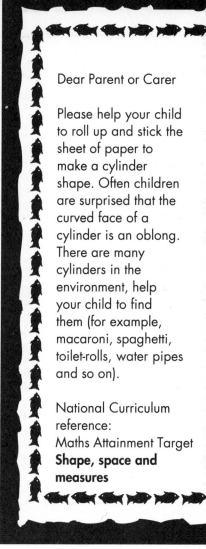

Dear Parent or Carer

Please help your child to roll up and stick the sheet of paper to make a cylinder shape. Often children are surprised that the curved face of a cylinder is an oblong. There are many cylinders in the environment, help your child to find them (for example, macaroni, spaghetti, toilet-rolls, water pipes and so on).

National Curriculum reference:
Maths Attainment Target
Shape, space and measures

_____and

child

_____

helper(s)

_____

did this activity together

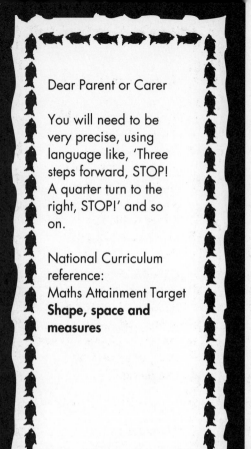

_____and

child

_____

helper(s)

_____

did this activity together

Walking round the table

● Ask an adult to stick an R for right on to your right hand.

● Can someone give you instructions for walking round some furniture.

● You must only move when given instructions and must follow all the instructions.

● Talk about left and right.

A newspaper bridge

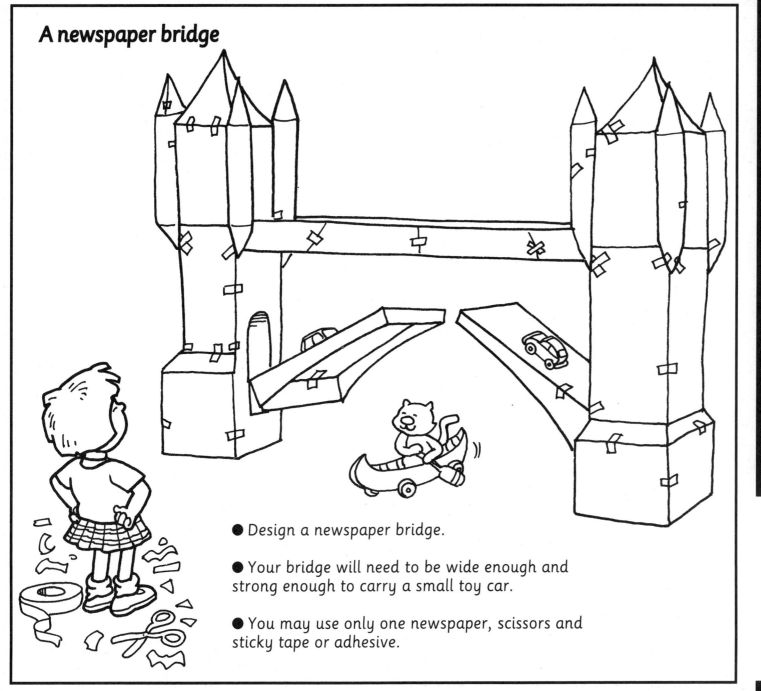

- Design a newspaper bridge.

- Your bridge will need to be wide enough and strong enough to carry a small toy car.

- You may use only one newspaper, scissors and sticky tape or adhesive.

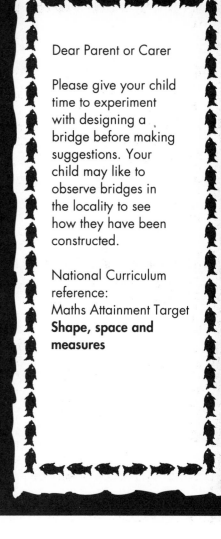

Dear Parent or Carer

Please give your child time to experiment with designing a bridge before making suggestions. Your child may like to observe bridges in the locality to see how they have been constructed.

National Curriculum reference:
Maths Attainment Target
Shape, space and measures

_____and

child

_____

helper(s)

_____

did this activity together

_____and

child

_____

helper(s)

_____

did this activity together

Three boxes

YOU WILL NEED: three cuboid boxes –
they will need to be of different sizes.

● Arrange your boxes in order of height.

● Will the boxes be in the same order if
you arrange them in terms of length or
of depth?

impact MATHS HOMEWORK

Faces

● Find a box. Look at the faces (sides).

● How many faces has your box?

● What shape are they?

● Are there any faces that are the same size?

● Draw face shapes to stick on to your favourite box.

● If possible, bring your decorated box into school.

_____and

child

_____

helper(s)

_____

did this activity together

Dear Parent or Carer

We are working on the recognition of right angles and bigger and smaller angles this week. We shall be drawing and finding right angles and right-angled shapes in class.

National Curriculum reference:
Maths Attainment Target
Shape, space and measures

_____and

child

_____

helper(s)

_____

did this activity together

Right-angled foods

● Which foods can you think of which have right angles in them?

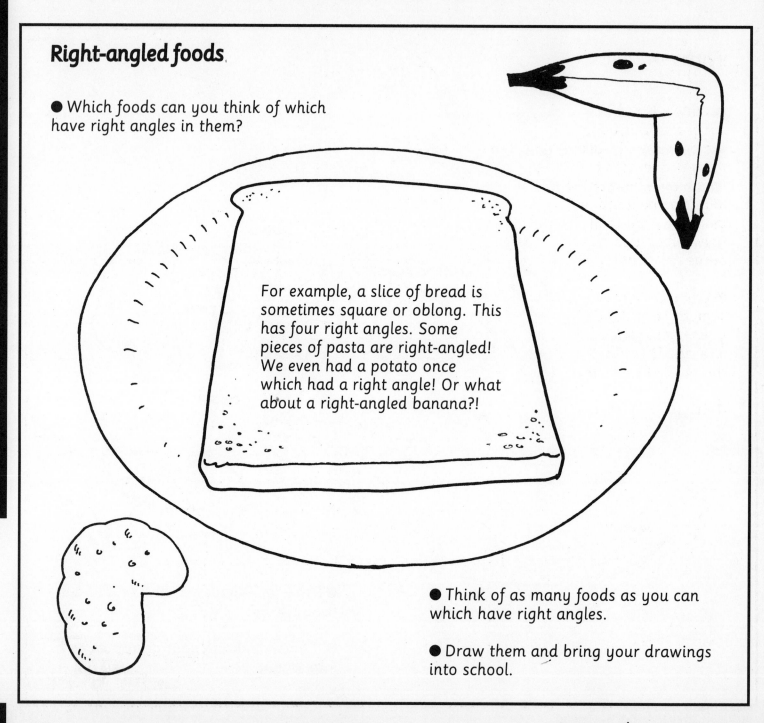

For example, a slice of bread is sometimes square or oblong. This has four right angles. Some pieces of pasta are right-angled! We even had a potato once which had a right angle! Or what about a right-angled banana?!

● Think of as many foods as you can which have right angles.

● Draw them and bring your drawings into school.

Pentagon search

● Which of the shapes on this page are pentagons? Talk to someone about which ones they think might be pentagons and colour all the ones which you both agree are pentagons.

● Can you find something around your home which is five-sided? Draw it on the back of this page.

● Bring your work into school.

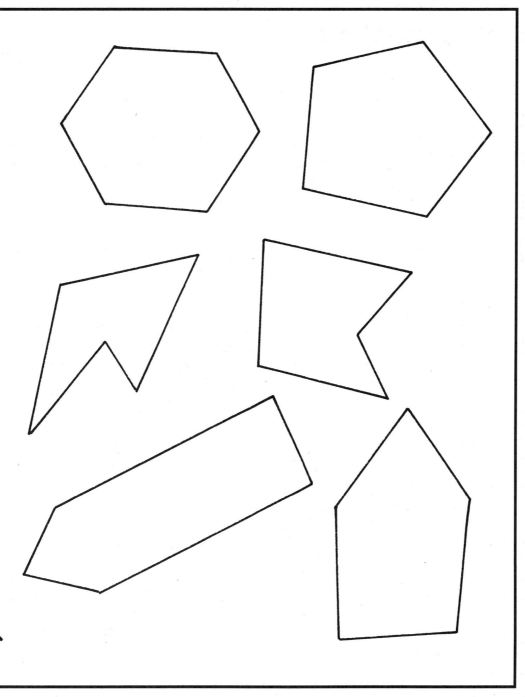

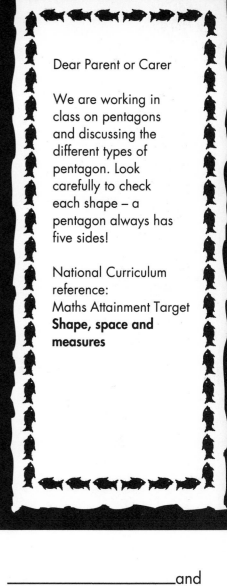

Dear Parent or Carer

We are working in class on pentagons and discussing the different types of pentagon. Look carefully to check each shape – a pentagon always has five sides!

National Curriculum reference:
Maths Attainment Target
Shape, space and measures

_____and

child

_____

helper(s)

_____

did this activity together

Hexagon search

● Which of the shapes on this page are hexagons?

● Talk to someone about which ones they think might be hexagons and colour all the ones which you both agree are hexagons.

● Can you find something around your home which is six-sided? Draw it on the back of this page.

● Bring your work into school.

Shape cost

● Draw a picture made up of the shapes shown below. You can use as many of each shape as you like, but your picture must only use these shapes and no others!

● Now look at the price list. Each shape is worth a certain amount of money. Add up what your picture is worth and write it down.

● Bring your picture into school.

Square 3ᴾ
Oblong 5ᴾ
Circle 4ᴾ
Triangle 2ᴾ
Hexagon 6ᴾ
Oval 1ᴾ

Dear Parent

Encourage your child to name the shapes. We are working on two-dimensional (that is, flat) shapes in class and we are trying to classify these by name.

National Curriculum reference:
Maths Attainment Target
Shape, space and measures

_____and

child

_____

helper(s)

_____

did this activity together

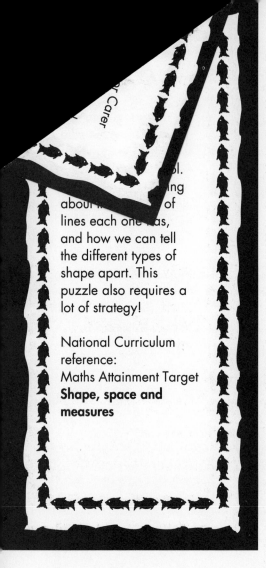

National Curriculum
reference:
Maths Attainment Target
**Shape, space and
measures**

_____and

child

_____

helper(s)

_____

did this activity together

Shape puzzle

● Cut out the shapes
at the side and bottom
of this page and
arrange them in this
grid so that there is a
triangle, an oblong and
a square in each row
and each column.

● Draw them in and
bring your completed
grid into school.

impact MATHS HOMEWORK

Building lines

- Go outside and look at the building you live in.

- Draw it. You could use the back of this page.

- How many vertical lines have you drawn?

- How many horizontal lines have you drawn?

- Bring your drawings back into school.

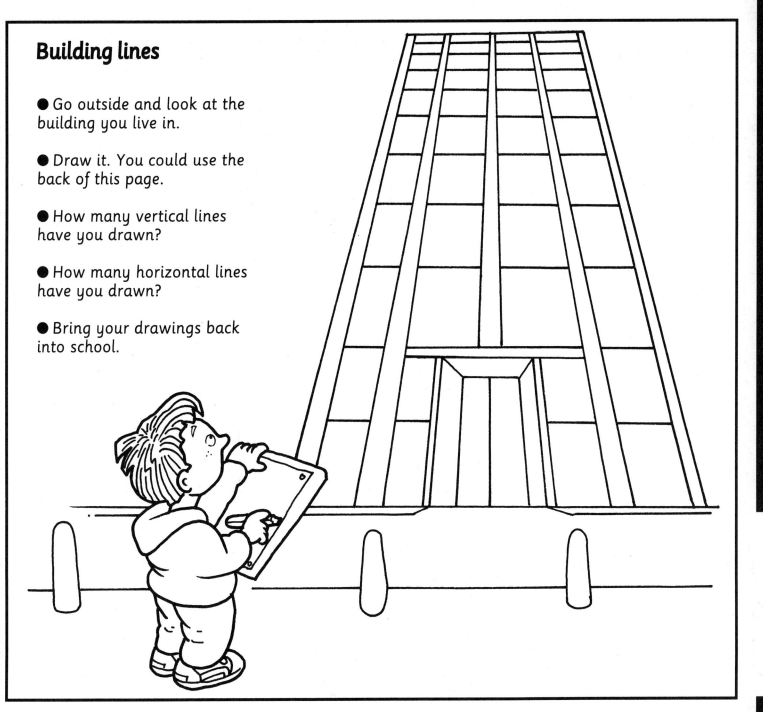

Dear Parent or Carer

We are discussing vertical and horizontal in class. Help your child to count accurately the number of each sort of line and write down the number.

National Curriculum reference:
Maths Attainment Target
Shape, space and measures

_____and

child

_____

helper(s)

_____

did this activity together

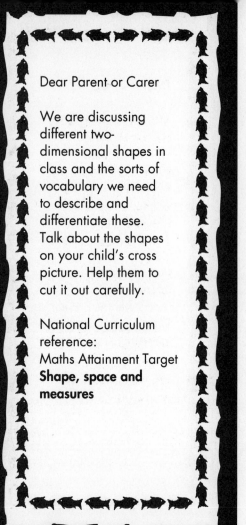
_____and

child

_____

helper(s)

_____

did this activity together

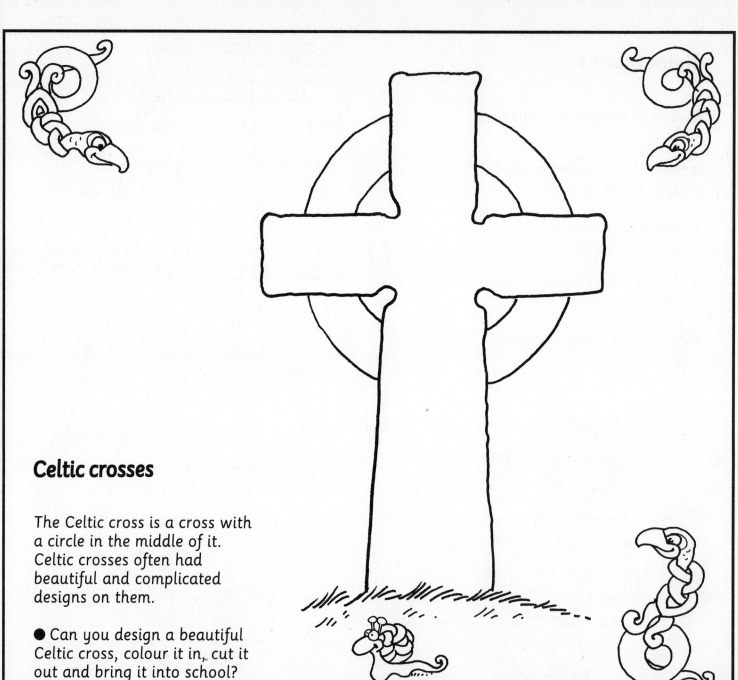

Celtic crosses

The Celtic cross is a cross with a circle in the middle of it. Celtic crosses often had beautiful and complicated designs on them.

● Can you design a beautiful Celtic cross, colour it in, cut it out and bring it into school?

Shape numbers

● Cut out the following shapes:

● What numbers can you make by arranging these shapes?

● Make as many as you can and draw round the shapes you use in each case. One has been done for you:

9 nine

Dear Parent or Carer

We are looking at two-dimensional shapes and the differences between them. This involves counting the numbers of sides and corners in each shape and looking at whether they have curly or straight lines.

National Curriculum reference:
Maths Attainment Target
Shape, space and measures

_____and

child

_____

helper(s)

_____

did this activity together

Corner count-up

● Draw a shape with four corners.

● Can you draw another different shape with four corners?

● Now draw a shape with three corners.

● Draw a shape with five corners! And one with six corners!

● Can you give each shape a name?

● Bring all your drawings into school.

Curly and straight

● Which numbers have straight lines in them?

● Which have curly lines?

● Look at all the numbers from 0 to 9 and decide which heading in this table they should go under. Then fill in the table:

straight lines	curly lines	straight and curly lines
7	**8**	**2**

Dear Parent or Carer

We are looking at two-dimensional shapes and which ones have straight lines (like a square) and which have curly lines (like a circle). This activity helps us with this, as well as reinforcing our numbers!

National Curriculum reference:
Maths Attainment Target
Shape, space and measures

_____and
child

_____
helper(s)

_____
did this activity together

Dear Parent or Carer

Try this activity with a
real sandwich. Before
cutting the bread,
give your child time
to consider how the
sandwich can be
halved. What shapes
will the new
sandwiches be? Will
they always be the
same shape? You
may like to supervise
your child and let him
or her cut the bread.

National Curriculum
reference:
Maths Attainment Target
**Shape, space and
measures**

_____and

child

_____

helper(s)

_____

did this activity together

Sandwiches

● Cut this
sandwich in
half – what
shapes do
you get?

● Try cutting
the sandwiches
in half again.
What shapes
do you get
this time?

impact MATHS HOMEWORK

Starry hexagons

● Can you see how this hexagon has become a star?

● Use the shape to make an even bigger star.

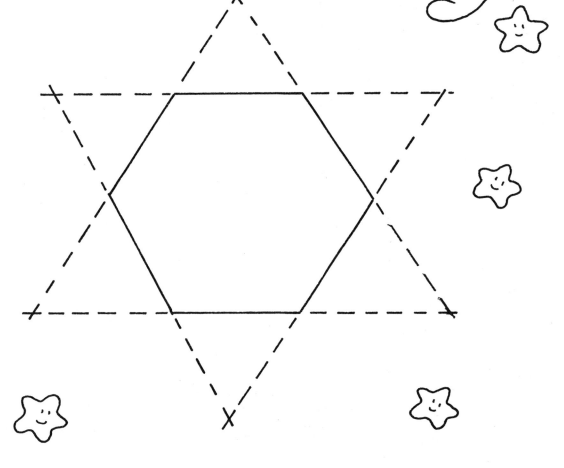

Dear Parent or Carer

Please give your child help with holding a ruler when extending the sides of the hexagon. You may like to make two or three different-sized stars which can be cut out, mounted on card and used as mobiles.

National Curriculum reference:
Maths Attainment Target
Shape, space and measures

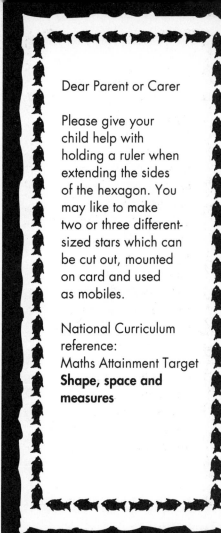

_____and

child

_____

helper(s)

_____

did this activity together

Dear Parent or Carer

Please help your child to arrange the table and to imagine what the bird's-eye view might look like. Your child will find this task easier using a large sheet of paper cut into the table shape before beginning. Try to identify the shapes that can be seen.

National Curriculum reference:
Maths Attainment Target
Shape, space and measures

_____and
child

_____
helper(s)

_____

did this activity together

Bird's-eye view

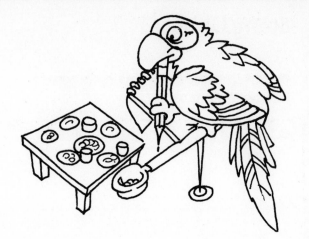

● Imagine that you are bird looking down at your meal table.

● Draw all the shapes that you can see and make sure that they are in the correct positions.

impact MATHS HOMEWORK

Looking from above

● Draw something interesting as seen from above.

Dear Parent or Carer

It is often difficult to identify objects from a bird's-eye view. This activity will help your child with early mapwork and drawing plans of rooms and so on. Your child may be encouraged to look at magazines that show different views of objects, such as cars, houses or gardens.

National Curriculum reference:
Maths Attainment Target
Shape, space and measures

_____and

child

_____

helper(s)

_____

did this activity together

_____and
child

_____

helper(s)

_____

did this activity together

My shape party hat

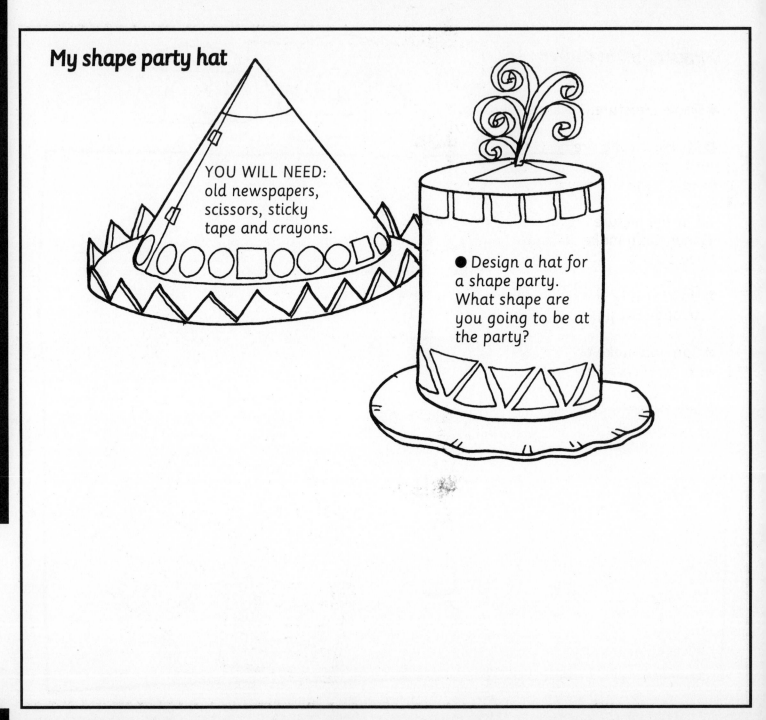

YOU WILL NEED: old newspapers, scissors, sticky tape and crayons.

● Design a hat for a shape party. What shape are you going to be at the party?

impact MATHS HOMEWORK

Make a jigsaw

● Draw a picture.

● Stick your picture on to card (an old birthday card or cereal packet would do).

● Cut the picture into a jigsaw. Only make straight-sided pieces.

● How quickly can you rearrange the jigsaw?

● Can you make the jigsaw with the pieces face down?

● Let someone else try.

_____and

child

_____

helper(s)

_____

did this activity together

_____and
child

_____
helper(s)

_____
did this activity together

Shape game

YOU WILL NEED: some paper, a pencil,
scissors and some LEGO bricks (or
raisins or pieces of pasta).

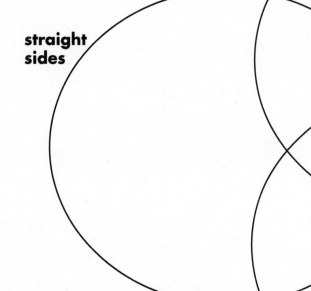

**straight
sides**

curved sides

non-symmetrical

HOW TO PLAY:
● Draw and cut out a shape.

● Your partner must place it in the
correct position on the Venn diagram –
if it is right, they take a LEGO brick (or
a raisin or a piece of pasta).

● Take turns; the first person to take
five bricks is the winner.

impact MATHS HOMEWORK

Hexagons

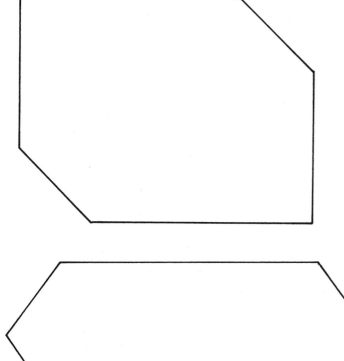

● Cut out these hexagons and stick them on to some cards.

● Can you design a tessellating pattern with each one?

● Do all hexagons tessellate?

● Try some other hexagonal shapes.

Dear Parent or Carer

Most children are familiar with regular shaped hexagons. Regular hexagons will always tessellate (that is, fit together without leaving any spaces). However, a hexagon is *any* shape with six straight sides. You may like to look at old buildings and very modern buildings to find examples of hexagonal patterns.

National Curriculum reference:
Maths Attainment Target
Shape, space and measures

_____and

child

_____

helper(s)

_____

did this activity together

_____and
child

_____
helper(s)

_____
did this activity together

Plasticine cubes

● Can you make a cube shape from Plasticine (or dough, pastry or bread)?

● How many faces has your cube?

● What shape are the faces?

● If your cube is cut in half, what shapes will you have?

● Draw the new shapes, can you describe them?

This is one way of cutting your cube in half.

impact MATHS HOMEWORK

Teachers' notes
Y E A R   T W O

Boxed-up! Display and talk about all the boxes that the children have made. Which ones are deepest? Do any have a square base? Perhaps they can make one in class that is very deep indeed! Can they find out which box holds the most and which holds the least by filling them with lentils or rice? Talk about other ways of making boxes; for example, using the traditional 'net'.

Two floor plans Can the children make any solid shapes they can name? Ask them to build a cube or a cuboid which will stand on two specified floor plans. Can they build a solid shape and then draw the floor plans of each of its faces so that someone else could build the same solid shape using just the floor plans? Can they make more than one cuboid using exactly 24 bricks? From which numbers of bricks can they make cubes?

Left, right The children can try out each other's routes. You will need to work with them in groups of three or four to do this, since both reading and following a series of numbered instructions are skills which take a lot of practice. Can they write a route for crossing the classroom safely, that is, without banging into any furniture? Talk about the number of turns needed.

Maze design A certain amount of intervention will probably be necessary as the children try out each other's mazes since some may not work very well! Talk about routes – how can we be sure that a route is 'good'? Discuss left and right – how do we remember these?

Cylinders and cones The children can compare their findings. How much more does the cylinder hold? Does it depend which way up they held the paper to make the cylinder? Try out long, thin cylinders and short, fat cylinders. Compare the volumes. Remember that the round in the middle which is not made of paper (the area of the contained floor), is bigger with the smaller, fatter cylinder.

Seven block puzzle The children can make different solid shapes in class and compare them. Can they make any solid shapes they can name? Ask them to build a cube or a cuboid using a specified number of bricks, such as 24. Can they make more than one shape of cuboid using 24 bricks? From which numbers of bricks can they make cubes? Write down the numbers of bricks they use to make a cube; for example 8, 27, 64 and 125. These are 'cube numbers' because we can make a cube from this number of bricks.

Seven block floor plan The children could make different solid shapes in class and compare them. Can they make any solid shapes they can name? Ask them to build a cube or cuboid which will stand on a specified floor plan. How many different cuboids or cubes can they make that will stand on that floor plan? What do the children notice about the numbers of bricks

used in each case? Can they make more than one shape of cuboid using exactly 24 bricks? From which numbers of bricks can they make cubes?

Turn around The children can put together four right angles (quarter circles) and make a circle. They should notice that two right angles make a straight line. It is possible to demonstrate that the corners of a triangle add up to a straight line by tearing up a triangle and laying the corners in a line – a template for this is provided at the back of the book on page 93. Can the children draw triangles with a right angle in? Can they draw a triangle with two right angles in? Can they explain why not? You may also like to extend this activity to discuss clockwise and anticlockwise turns.

Corner cut-out The children can compare their shapes. They will all be types of trapezium – this is a four-sided shape with two parallel sides. A trapezium is a special type of quadrilateral. Other special quadrilaterals are squares (four equal sides and four right angles) and oblongs (four right angles and two pairs of equal sides). Both squares and oblongs are rectangles!

Door angles The children can measure their angles using templates of 90° and 45° angles. (These are provided on page 93 of this book.) Discuss the fact that 45° is exactly half a right angle, and that 135° is a right angle plus another 45°. Talk about how many right angles make a straight line and how many make a full circle. How many 45° angles make a straight line and how many make a full circle?

Build a model You will need a box of coloured cubes. Turn your back on the

children and make a model using a small number of cubes, then give them instructions explaining how you made the model. Can all the children make the model from your instructions? How many were the same? What was difficult? How could the instructions have been improved? Can the children draw their models? How are they going to indicate the fact that two bricks are on top of one another?

Bike wheel The children could arrange themselves in order according to the length of string/one revolution. Which wheel has the longest and which the shortest circumference? Which is the biggest circle? What do we understand by the biggest circle?

Making quadrilaterals How many different shapes have the children made? Can they arrange the quadrilaterals in different groups and explain their similarities and differences? Ask a group of children to turn round while one child describes a quadrilateral – can the group guess which one it is? Encourage the children to use the words: 'right angle', 'bigger', 'smaller', 'opposite' and 'parallel'. These quadrilaterals, when put in groups, would make super mobiles. Talk about the types of quadrilateral.

Designing quadrilaterals This is an activity which will help children to build up a shape vocabulary: 'opposite', 'larger or smaller than a right angle', 'parallel' and so on. The children could make their quadrilaterals into mobiles and arrange them into sets, for example, those with four sides of equal length, those with three sides of equal length and those with two sides of equal length. How many different ways of sorting can the children discover?

Triangles Are the children able to arrange their triangles into the three sets and give the criteria for their sorting? Perhaps they could work in groups and write instructions for making their triangles and/or a description of their triangles. The triangles could be used as mobiles and hung up and their descriptions and instructions displayed alongside. If you draw a triangle and cut it out, you can show that all three angles make a straight line by cutting off the angles and lining them up. A template for this is provided on page 93 of this book.

Turn, turn, turn again This activity is fun to do at the beginning or at the end of PE time. You may like to use the term '90°' for a quarter turn. Ask the children questions such as, 'If we jump a half turn (two 90° turns), what will we be looking at? How many 90° turns are there before we are back where we started?' Discuss clockwise and anticlockwise here also.

How many corners do you turn? The children could make jointed model people using strips of card and split paper fasteners. These could be arranged to show many of the different right angle shapes that can be made with the body.

Bedroom view The children can begin to draw objects to scale, perhaps using their table first. A ruler length, book length or handspan length could be represented by a LEGO brick. Their scale table pictures can then be cut out and arranged on a large sheet of paper that represents the size and the shape of the classroom. Each child could draw their portrait and position it in

the appropriate place in the classroom plan. Extended this to incorporate other pieces of classroom furniture.

Letter symmetry Do the children agree about whether the letters are horizontally or vertically symmetrical? They could work in pairs, each designing a Multilink or peg board pattern on half the board, for their partners to complete symmetrically.

Rotational symmetry The designs will make a very colourful display and can lead to work on other types of symmetry. Different rotations could be introduced; for example, 90°, 180° and so on. How many 90° turns are needed before the picture returns to its original position? Check this by holding up one picture to show the class, then ask them all to turn away and rotate the picture through 90°. When the children turn back, can they tell if you have rotated the picture or not?

Patchwork fractions The children could create a big patchwork 'quilt' with their patterns. New patterns could be created by colouring quarters of the squares. These smaller shapes could make a border for the quilt. Try an investigation using a 4 × 4 grid. The children must colour half the squares in red. How many different ways can they find of doing this?

Windy days It is very important that the children have had some experience of the points of the compass before taking this activity home. They can collate their information and it can be entered on to a database. Let them build up weather data over a longer period of time. Do we have different types of weather depending on the wind direction?

Design a box How many different-shaped boxes are there? Can the children sort and order their boxes? Do all the boxes carry the object safely? If not, how could the design be improved? Talk about the ways in which they made their boxes. Show them some different nets; for example, the net of a cube, cuboid or tetrahedron.

Wrapping eight bricks Try this as an investigation in school using eight cubes of the same size. How many different cuboids can be made? Can the children explain the different arrangements? Why do they need different-sized and/or shaped paper for wrapping them? The brick boxes could be used in a class post office. This activity could then include weighing and pricing the parcels.

Guess where I am Make a large grid on a display board and label the rows and columns. The children can place pictures or models on the squares with another child giving either the grid number or specifying on to which square the picture is going to be placed.

Where the sun shines The children can attempt to arrange the pictures of their homes so that they are correctly orientated to a compass picture and sorted for where the sun shines at different times of the day. How many children have bedrooms facing north, south, east or west? Extend this activity to observing the Sun's apparent position around the school during the day.

Where do these shapes fit? The children could draw quadrilaterals, hexagons, pentagons and triangles and sort them into families. These could be

coloured and used as the leaves on different trees in a display. The trees could then be labelled, for example, 'The tree with hexagonal leaves', and so on.

Magical rings These circles would make super festival decorations. Talk about the fact that this strip has only one face. If we start colouring it in, we will wind up colouring both sides! What happens if we cut along the line made by the fly down the middle of the strip? Try it and see!

Mr Cube The children may like to arrange a 'square party' for their toys. The playdough food would need to be cube-shaped and arranged on square plates. Can the children design and make square hats for their toys? Discuss the fact that some cuboids have two square faces and four oblong faces. A pyramid may have one square face (the base). Are there any other shapes which have a least one square face?

Pentominoes The children can use the 1cm squared paper provided on page 92 of this book to record their pentomino patterns. How many different pentominoes have the children found? (There are 12 different ones in all.) How do the children know that each pentomino is different? Can the pentominoes be arranged in sets? What criteria can be used for the sorting?

Getting bigger The children's drawings will make a wonderful display. To extend the activity, ask them to design fatter and/or thinner dogs on their own grids. This activity helps children to think of scale as increasing or decreasing the size of objects.

Boxed-up!

YOU WILL NEED: scissors and sticky tape.

● Use the oblong on this page to make a box by cutting out the corners and folding up the sides.

● You could fix the sides together with sticky tape.

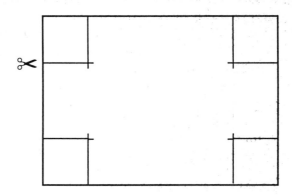

● Bring your box into school.

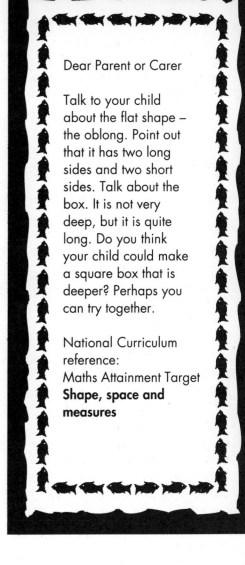

Dear Parent or Carer

Talk to your child about the flat shape – the oblong. Point out that it has two long sides and two short sides. Talk about the box. It is not very deep, but it is quite long. Do you think your child could make a square box that is deeper? Perhaps you can try together.

National Curriculum reference:
Maths Attainment Target
Shape, space and measures

_____and

child

_____

helper(s)

_____

did this activity together

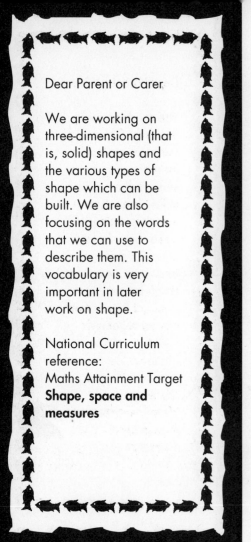
Two floor plans

YOU WILL NEED: seven Multilink cubes.

● Using the cubes, build a model which will fit on this floor plan. The base of it must cover these spaces exactly.

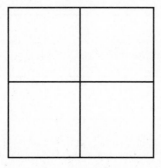

● Now look at your model. If you turn it on its side, will it fit on this second floor plan?

● Try to modify it so that it will.

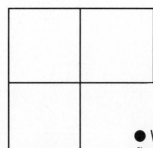

● When you think it will fit on both floor plans draw your model carefully on the back of this page.

Left, right

● Plan a route for your teddy to take around one of the rooms in your house. It must take him from one side of the room to the other. He can turn left, turn right, and walk as many paces as necessary.

● Ask someone to write down his route for you opposite as a series of numbered instructions.

For example:

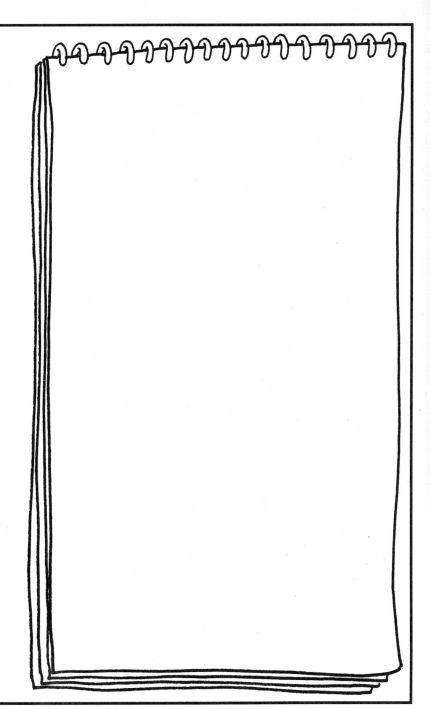

1. Enter kitchen

2. Turn left

3. Move 4 paces forward

4. Turn right

5. Move 8 paces forward

● Bring your routes into school.

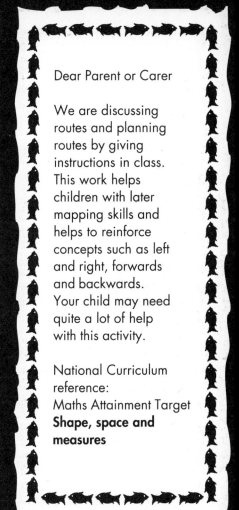

Dear Parent or Carer

We are discussing routes and planning routes by giving instructions in class. This work helps children with later mapping skills and helps to reinforce concepts such as left and right, forwards and backwards. Your child may need quite a lot of help with this activity.

National Curriculum reference:
Maths Attainment Target
Shape, space and measures

_____and

child

_____

helper(s)

_____

did this activity together

_____and

child

_____

helper(s)

_____

did this activity together

Maze design

● Can you design and draw a maze? (It doesn't have to be as complicated as this one!)

YOU WILL NEED: lots of scrap paper and someone to help you.

● What creatures will you put in the middle?

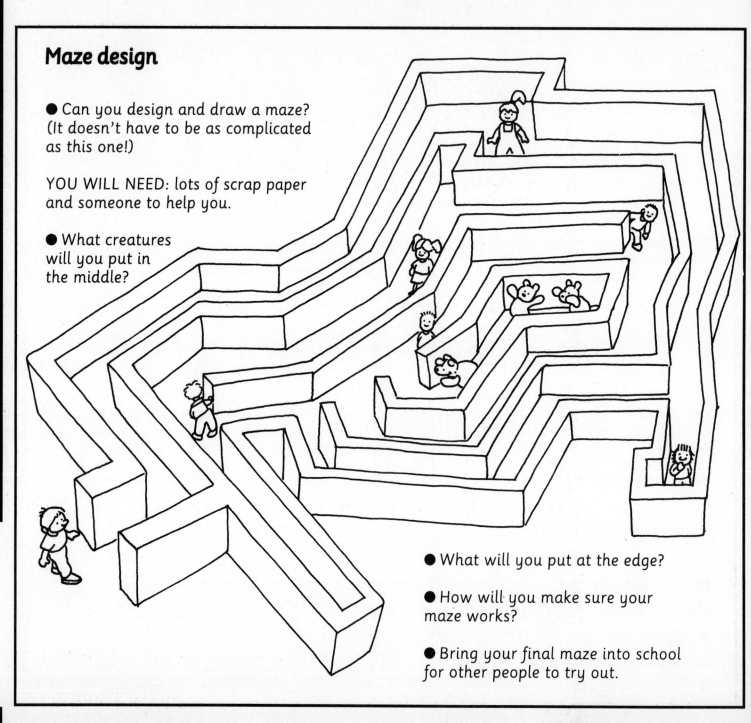

● What will you put at the edge?

● How will you make sure your maze works?

● Bring your final maze into school for other people to try out.

impact MATHS HOMEWORK

Cylinders and cones

● Take an A4 (29.5cm × 21cm) sheet of paper and some sticky tape.

● Make a cylinder.

● With another A4 sheet of paper, make a cone.

● Which one holds the most? Try to find out by using rice or lentils or dried pasta or even sugar (a bit messy!).

● Report back to class on your findings.

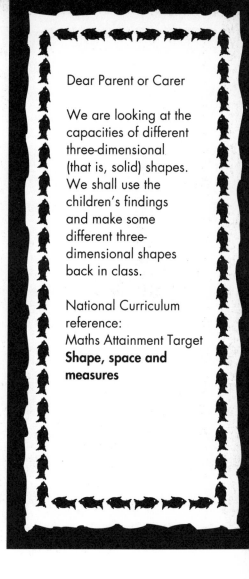

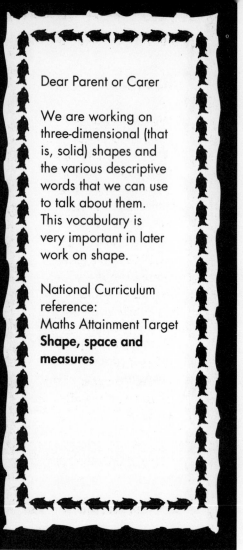

_____and

child

_____

helper(s)

_____

did this activity together

Seven block puzzle

YOU WILL NEED: seven Multilink blocks, a piece of paper and a pencil.

● You or your helper builds a model using the seven blocks and draws it carefully. THE OTHER PERSON IS NOT ALLOWED TO LOOK AT IT. Then the model-builder breaks up the model.

● Sitting back to back, the model-builder must describe the model to the second person in such a way that they can build it correctly themselves.

● When the second person has finished, compare their building with the drawing. Were they correct?

● Now have a go the other way round; so that the other person builds and draws the model and their partner must build it from the description.

● Bring both your drawings into school.

Seven block floor plan

YOU WILL NEED: seven Multilink cubes.

● Can you build a model using the cubes which will fit on this floor plan? The base of it must cover these spaces exactly.

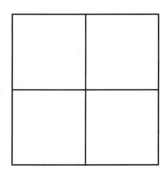

● Draw your model carefully. You could use the back of this page.

● Can you make another different model which will cover the same floor plan?

● If you can, draw that one as well! Can you make some more?

● Bring all your drawings into school.

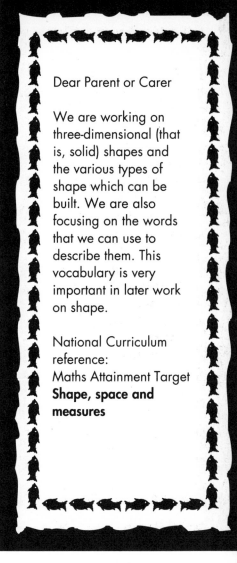

Dear Parent or Carer

We are working on three-dimensional (that is, solid) shapes and the various types of shape which can be built. We are also focusing on the words that we can use to describe them. This vocabulary is very important in later work on shape.

National Curriculum reference:
Maths Attainment Target
Shape, space and measures

_____and

child

_____

helper(s)

_____

did this activity together

_____and
child

_____
helper(s)

did this activity together

Turn around

YOU WILL NEED: a coin, some counters (raisins would do!) and a teddy bear each.

● Sit both teddies facing towards the front.

● Take it in turns with a helper to spin the coin.

● If the coin lands heads, turn your teddy one right angle to the left.

● If the coin lands tails, turn your teddy one right angle to the right.

● The first person whose teddy turns a complete circle in either direction is the winner!

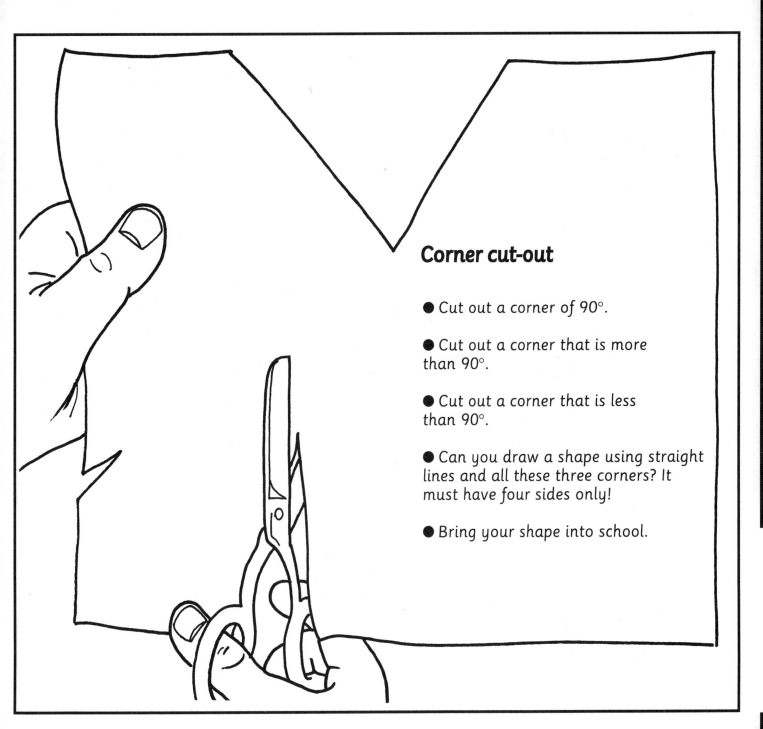

Corner cut-out

● Cut out a corner of 90°.

● Cut out a corner that is more than 90°.

● Cut out a corner that is less than 90°.

● Can you draw a shape using straight lines and all these three corners? It must have four sides only!

● Bring your shape into school.

_____and

child

_____

helper(s)

_____

did this activity together

_____and

child

_____

helper(s)

_____

did this activity together

Door angles

● Find a door which will open very wide – more than 90°.

● Open the door to half a right angle. Put a piece of paper under the door and draw the angle between the door and where it is when it is closed.

● Open the door so that it makes a right angle. Now put a piece of paper under it and draw the right angle.

● Open the door another half right angle (if possible) – or as wide as you can – and draw this angle on another piece of paper.

● Open the door to 180° (if possible) – or as wide as you can – and draw this angle on another piece of paper.

● Bring all your pieces of paper into school.

impact MATHS HOMEWORK

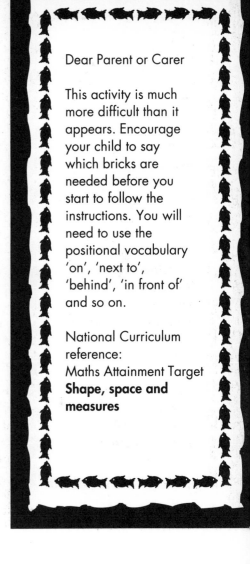

Dear Parent or Carer

This activity is much more difficult than it appears. Encourage your child to say which bricks are needed before you start to follow the instructions. You will need to use the positional vocabulary 'on', 'next to', 'behind', 'in front of' and so on.

National Curriculum reference:
Maths Attainment Target
Shape, space and measures

Build a model

YOU WILL NEED: several bricks in different sizes and colours, begin with about six bricks each.

● Sit opposite each other with a book between you so that your partner cannot see what you are doing.

● Build a simple model using about four bricks and describe it to the person opposite, so that the instructions allow an identical model to be built.

● Check the results by comparing the finished models and then reverse roles.

_____and

child

_____

helper(s)

_____

did this activity together

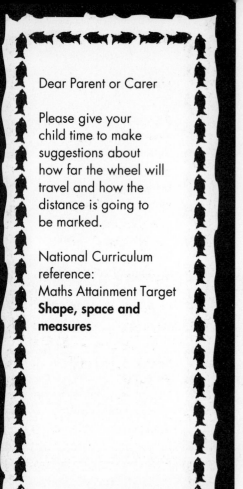

Dear Parent or Carer

Please give your child time to make suggestions about how far the wheel will travel and how the distance is going to be marked.

National Curriculum reference:
Maths Attainment Target
Shape, space and measures

_____and

child

_____

helper(s)

_____

did this activity together

Bike wheel

● How far does your bike wheel travel in one revolution (one complete turn)? Find out!

● How will you know where to begin and where to finish measuring?

● Bring a piece of string into school to show how far your wheel travelled.

Making quadrilaterals

A quadrilateral is a four-sided shape.

● Cut four strips of paper; two that are 10cm long and two that are 7cm long.

● Arrange them in as many closed ways as you can and draw round the shapes you make.

● Stick the strips together in your favourite shape.

● Can you name any of the shapes that you have made?

0 1 2 3 4 5 6 7 8 9 10
one decimetre

impact MATHS HOMEWORK

_____and

child

_____

helper(s)

_____

did this activity together

_____and

child

_____

helper(s)

_____

did this activity together

Designing quadrilaterals

A quadrilateral is a shape which has four straight sides and four angles (corners).

YOU WILL NEED: several strips of card (cut from birthday or Christmas cards or from cereal boxes) and some adhesive or sticky tape.

● Use the strips to make some quadrilaterals, stick the corners together to make your shapes.

● Make about six different-shaped quadrilaterals to bring into school.

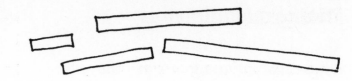

This is one quadrilateral you could design with these strips.

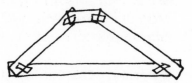

Triangles

● Can you design three types of triangle?

● For each triangle you will need three strips of card (cut up old birthday or Christmas cards or cereal boxes).

● An equilateral triangle needs three strips of equal length.

● An isosceles triangle needs two equal length strips and one of a different length.

● A scalene triangle needs three unequal length strips.

Dear Parent or Carer

Your child may need help with measuring the strips. Give them time for experimenting with the strips before sticking them. Your child might like to extend this activity by making several different-shaped triangles for each set.

National Curriculum reference:
Maths Attainment Target
Shape, space and measures

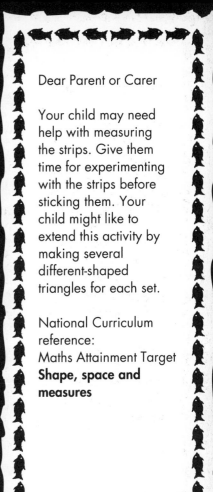

_____and
child

_____
helper(s)

_____

did this activity together

Turn, turn, turn again

● Stand in the middle of a room at home.

● Ask somebody to give you these instructions.
• A quarter turn to the right (clockwise) – what are you looking at?
• Another quarter turn to the right (clockwise) – what do you see now?
• Keep going until you are back where you started.

● How many turns did you make?

● Can you jump a half turn?

● How many quarter turns is this the same as?

impact MATHS HOMEWORK

How many corners do you turn?

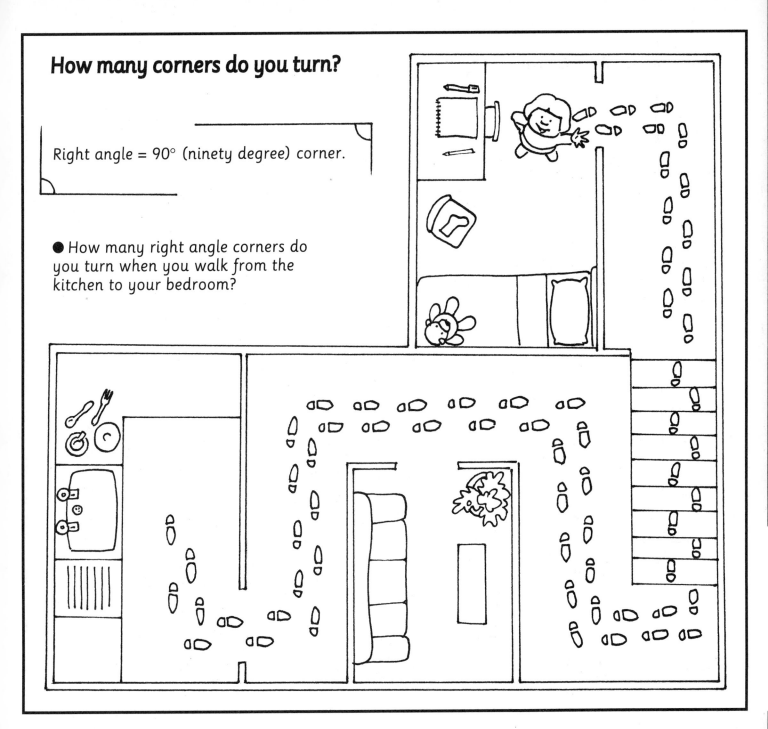

Right angle = 90° (ninety degree) corner.

● How many right angle corners do you turn when you walk from the kitchen to your bedroom?

Dear Parent or Carer

Talk to your child about right angles. Many joints in our bodies can be positioned at 90°. Your child could make interesting body shapes and count the number of right angles in each body shape.

National Curriculum reference:
Maths Attainment Target
Shape, space and measures

_____and

child

_____

helper(s)

_____

did this activity together

_____and

child

_____

helper(s)

_____

did this activity together

Bedroom view

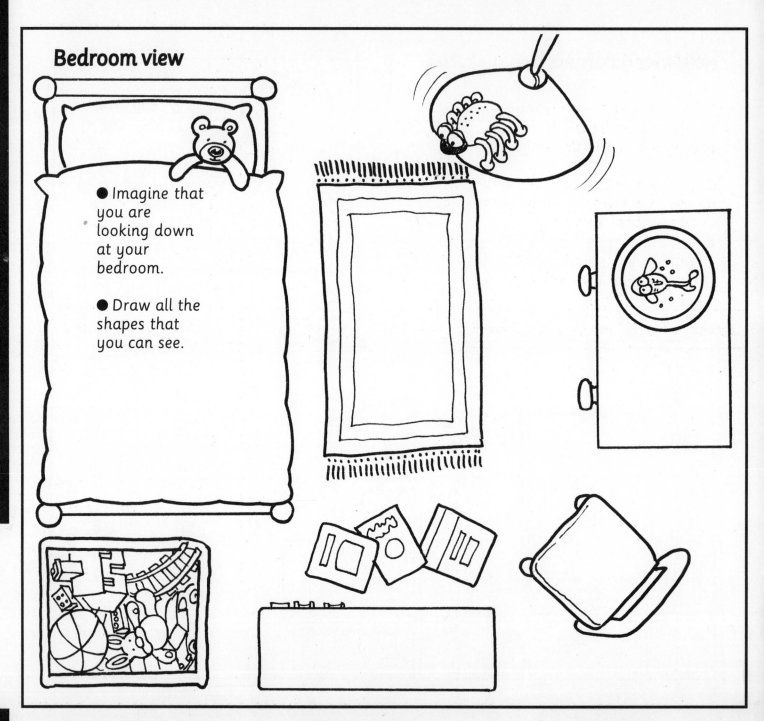

● Imagine that you are looking down at your bedroom.

● Draw all the shapes that you can see.

impact MATHS HOMEWORK

Letter symmetry

YOU WILL NEED: a small mirror and all the capital letters of the alphabet written out on old Christmas cards.

● Put the mirror on each letter in turn to investigate whether it has horizontal and/or vertical symmetry.

● Fill in the table below to record your findings and bring them into school.

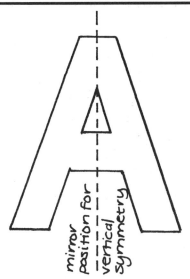

mirror position for vertical symmetry

Letter	Horizontally symmetrical	Vertically symmetrical	Not symmetrical
A	✗	✔	✗

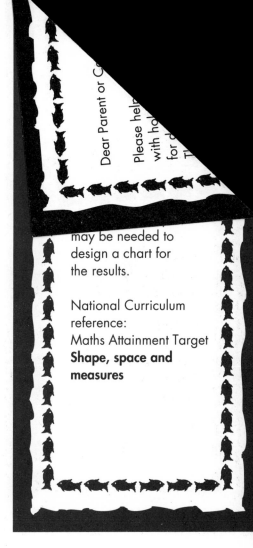

Dear Parent or C

Please hel
with h
for

may be needed to design a chart for the results.

National Curriculum reference:
Maths Attainment Target
Shape, space and measures

_____and

child

_____

helper(s)

_____

did this activity together

Rotational symmetry

● Cut out a card square
like this. Draw an
interesting shape in one
corner and cut it out
carefully.

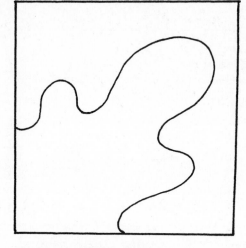

● You are going to draw round this
shape as you rotate it. Like this:

● Bring your shape and your pattern
into school.

impact MATHS HOMEWORK

Patchwork fractions

● Colour half the squares below in black.

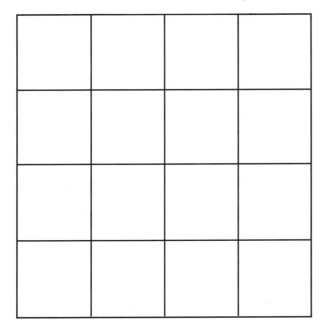

● Choose your favourite pattern and stick it down. Bring it into school.

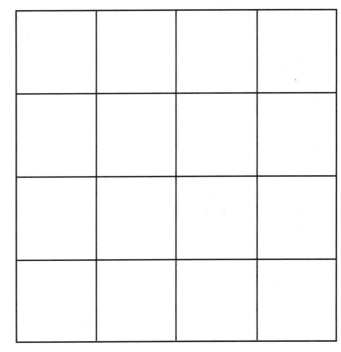

● Cut up all the squares and arrange them within the 4 × 4 square opposite.

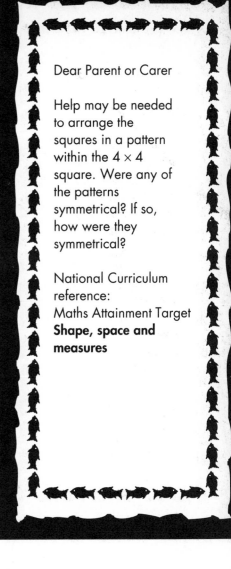

Dear Parent or Carer

Help may be needed to arrange the squares in a pattern within the 4 × 4 square. Were any of the patterns symmetrical? If so, how were they symmetrical?

National Curriculum reference:
Maths Attainment Target
Shape, space and measures

_____and

child

_____

helper(s)

_____

did this activity together

impact MATHS HOMEWORK

_____and

child

_____

helper(s)

_____

did this activity together

Windy days

● From which direction is the wind blowing today?

● Keep a chart to show the direction of the wind every day for a week.

Day	Today the wind is blowing from the...
Saturday	
Sunday	
Monday	
Tuesday	
Wednesday	
Thursday	
Friday	

impact MATHS HOMEWORK

Design a box

● Design a box to hold safely something that rolls around, such as an egg, a ball or some marbles.

HINT: Start with an old box and experiment.

● If your box is too big, how could you make it smaller?

● Your finished box must be a close fit. Making a big box and filling it with, say, scrunched-up newspaper is CHEATING!

● Which shape of box will you try first?

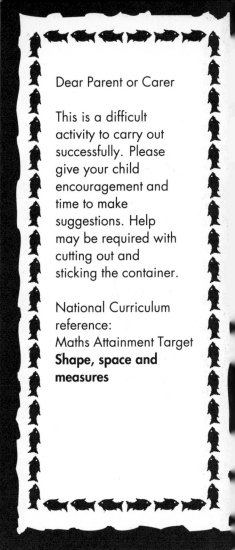

Dear Parent or Carer

This is a difficult activity to carry out successfully. Please give your child encouragement and time to make suggestions. Help may be required with cutting out and sticking the container.

National Curriculum reference:
Maths Attainment Target
Shape, space and measures

_____and

child

_____

helper(s)

_____

did this activity together

impact MATHS HOMEWORK

_____and

child

_____

helper(s)

did this activity together

Wrapping eight bricks

● How many ways can you arrange eight bricks to wrap them up?

● Which way do you think is the best for wrapping?

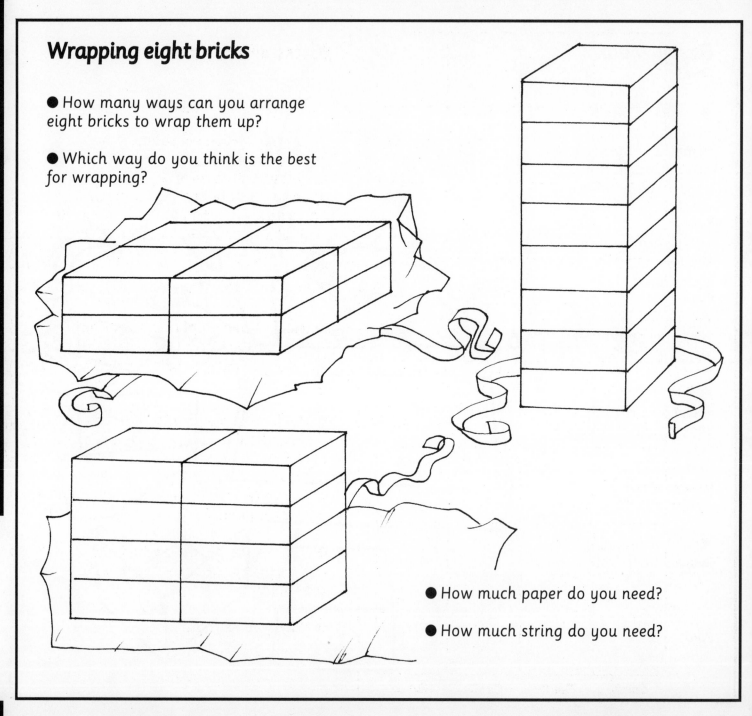

● How much paper do you need?

● How much string do you need?

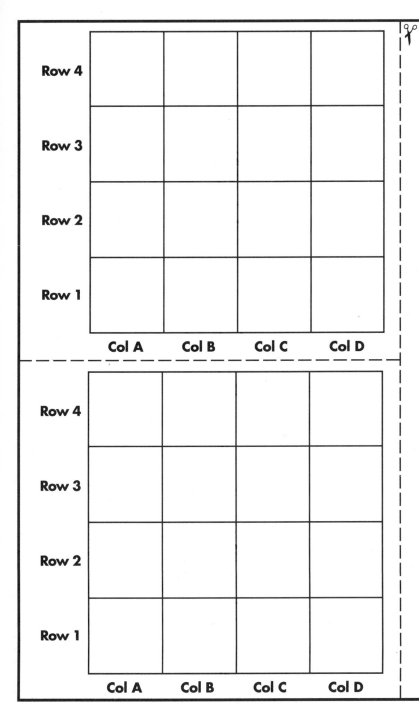

Guess where I am

A game for two players.

YOU WILL NEED: six counters or buttons for each player and a book (as a divider) to ensure that the opposing grid board cannot be seen. You could cut out the two grid boards and stick them on to some card to strengthen them.

HOW TO PLAY:

● The first person places a counter in a square on their grid board and explains its position. For example, I say 'Column C, row 2.'.

● The second player places a counter in the corresponding square on their grid board.

● Continue until all the counters have been positioned.

● Remove the divider and compare the counter positions – are they all the same?

● Now reverse roles.

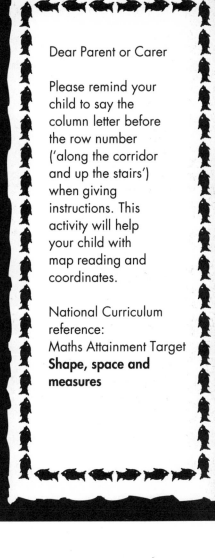

Dear Parent or Carer

Please remind your child to say the column letter before the row number ('along the corridor and up the stairs') when giving instructions. This activity will help your child with map reading and coordinates.

National Curriculum reference:
Maths Attainment Target
Shape, space and measures

_____and

child

_____

helper(s)

_____

did this activity together

_____and

child

_____

helper(s)

_____

did this activity together

Where the sun shines

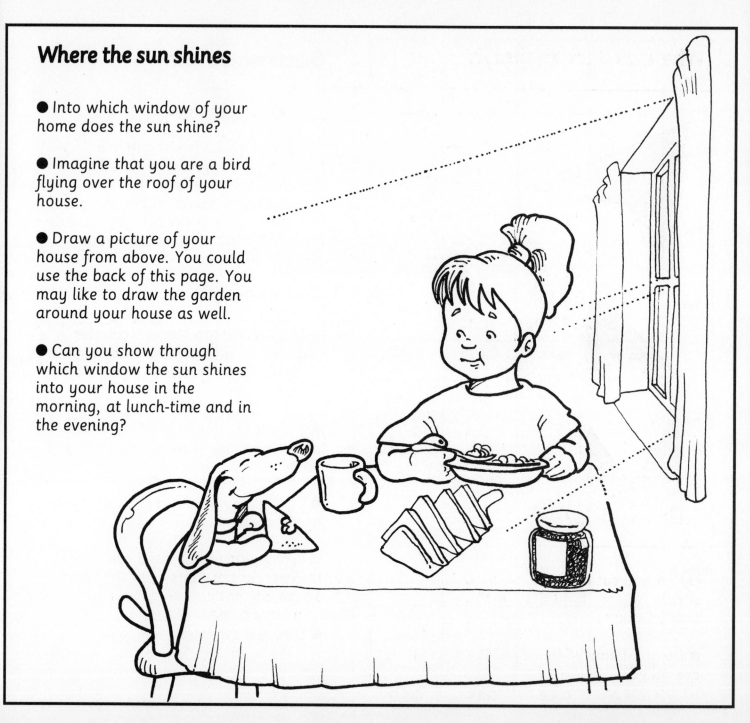

● Into which window of your
home does the sun shine?

● Imagine that you are a bird
flying over the roof of your
house.

● Draw a picture of your
house from above. You could
use the back of this page. You
may like to draw the garden
around your house as well.

● Can you show through
which window the sun shines
into your house in the
morning, at lunch-time and in
the evening?

impact MATHS HOMEWORK

Where do these shapes fit?

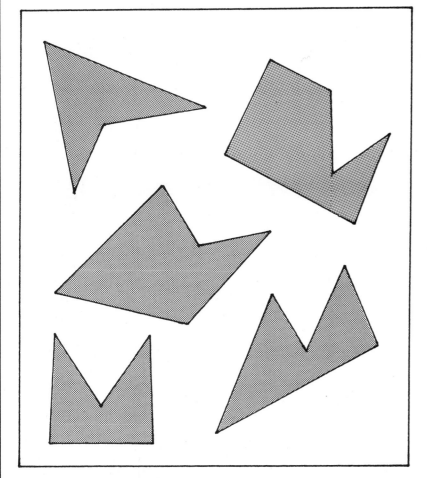

● Can you cut out the unshaded shapes and try to fit them into the shaded spaces?

● Do you know what any of the shapes are called?

● Write a description of your favourite shape, so that we can guess which one you have chosen.

_____and

child

_____

helper(s)

_____

did this activity together

_____and
child

_____
helper(s)

_____
did this activity together

Magical rings

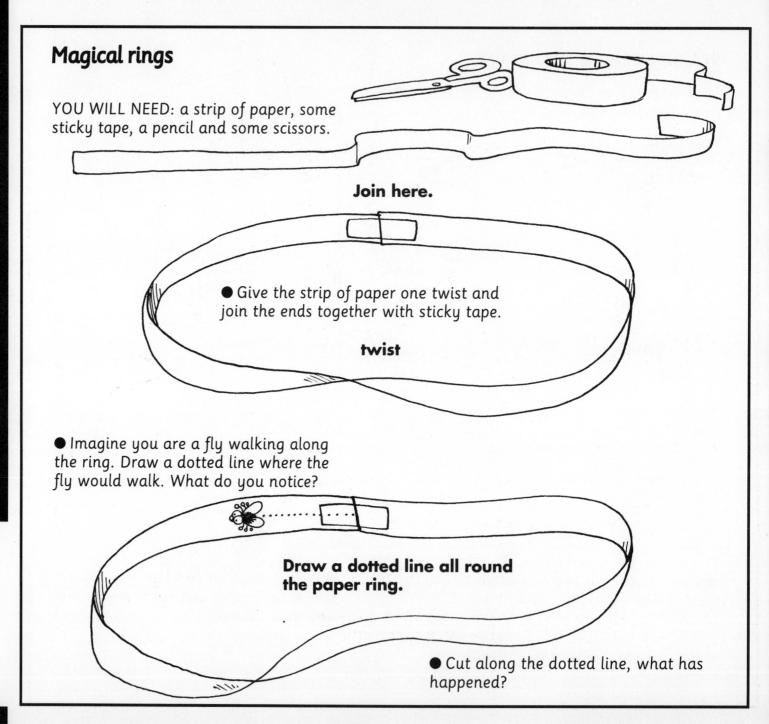

YOU WILL NEED: a strip of paper, some sticky tape, a pencil and some scissors.

Join here.

● Give the strip of paper one twist and join the ends together with sticky tape.

twist

● Imagine you are a fly walking along the ring. Draw a dotted line where the fly would walk. What do you notice?

Draw a dotted line all round the paper ring.

● Cut along the dotted line, what has happened?

impact MATHS HOMEWORK

Mr Cube

Mr Cube is coming to tea. He likes everything to have a square face.

● Design a mug for him to have his tea in.

● Try making the mug from old newspapers and sticky tape.

Dear Parent or Carer

Please give your child time to experiment with newspaper and sticky tape before deciding upon the final design. Your child may like to use a box or cardboard from old Christmas or birthday cards to assist with making the mug.

National Curriculum reference:
Maths Attainment Target
Shape, space and measures

_____and

child

_____

helper(s)

_____

did this activity together

_____and

child

_____

helper(s)

_____

did this activity together

Pentominoes

YOU WILL NEED: the five squares on this page cut out, a pencil or crayon and a piece of 1cm squared paper.

● Try out different arrangements using the five squares. How many different shapes can you make with them? (The squares must join with a whole edge NOT just at a corner.)

● Record all your shapes on 1cm squared paper.

Getting bigger

● What do you think you would need
to do to make this dog even bigger?

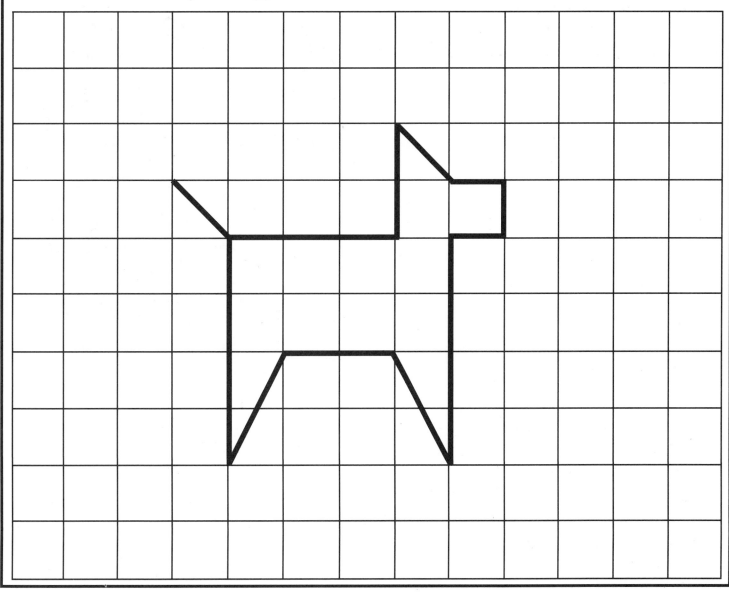

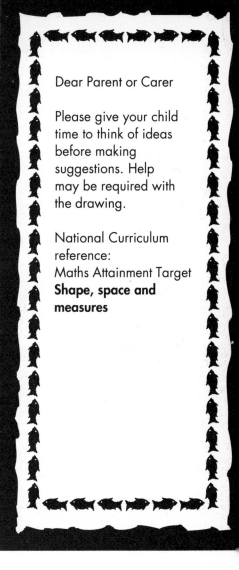

Dear Parent or Carer

Please give your child
time to think of ideas
before making
suggestions. Help
may be required with
the drawing.

National Curriculum
reference:
Maths Attainment Target
**Shape, space and
measures**

_____and

child

_____

helper(s)

_____

did this activity together

impact MATHS HOMEWORK

1cm squared paper

impact MATHS HOMEWORK

Templates

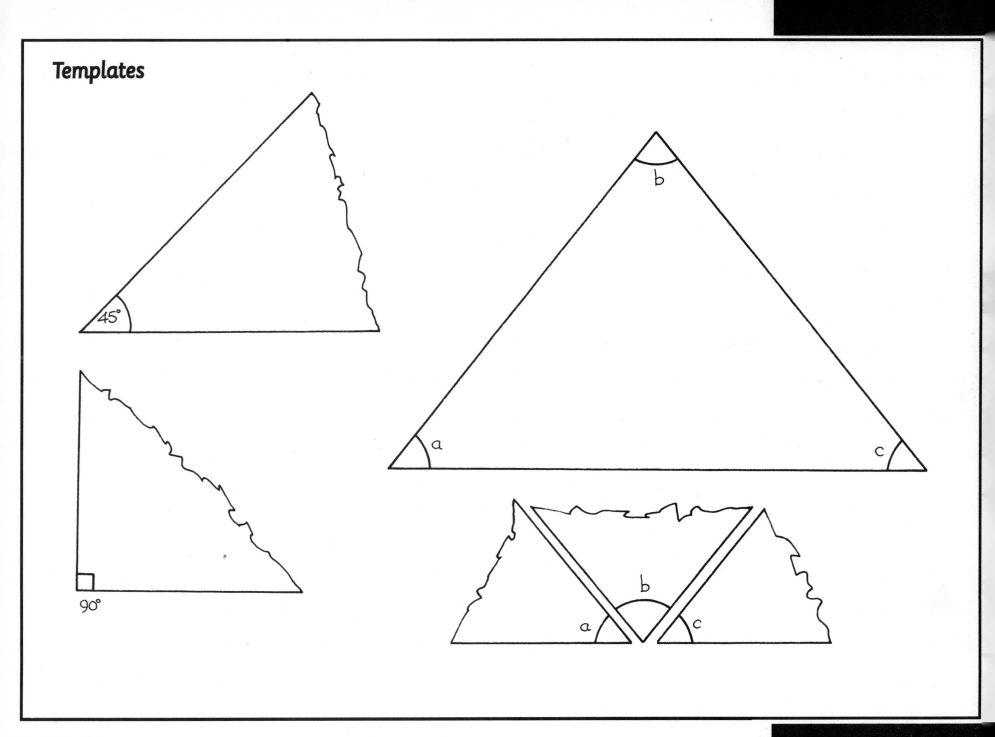

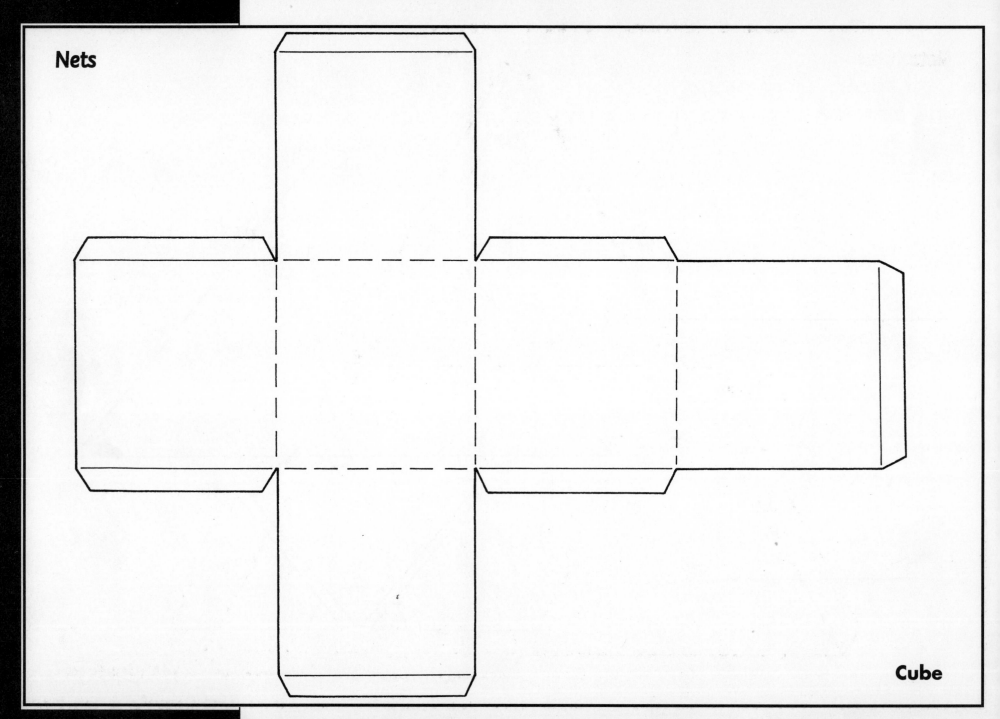

Cube

impact MATHS HOMEWORK

Nets

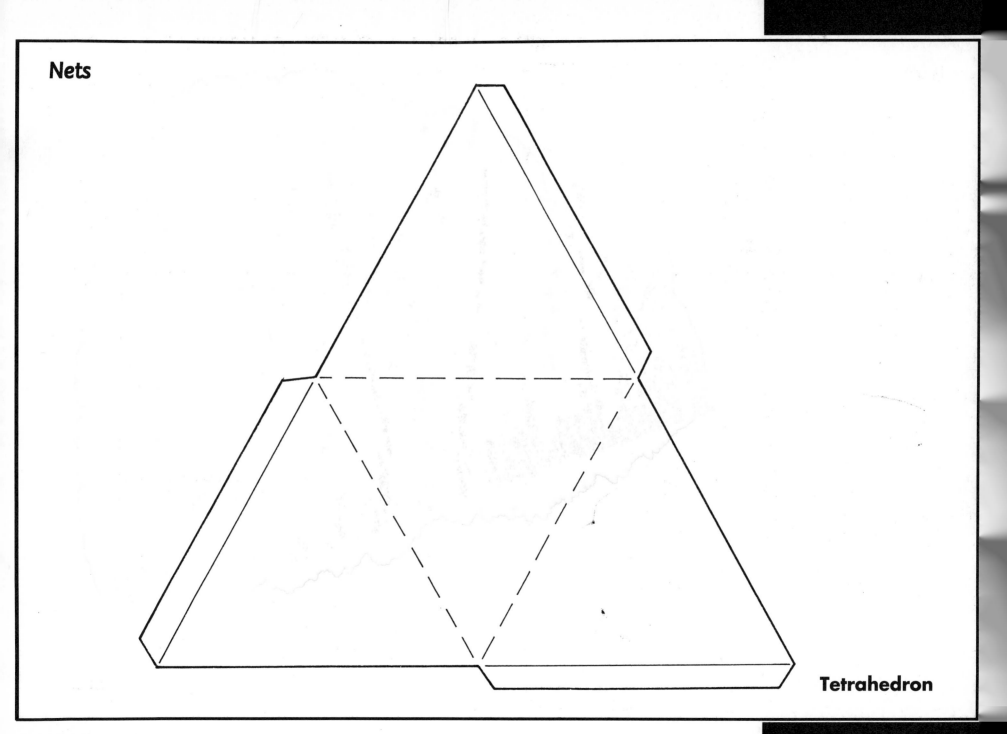

Tetrahedron

IMPACT diaries

The IMPACT diaries provide a mechanism by means of which an efficient parent-teacher dialogue is established. Through these diaries, which last up to two years depending upon the frequency of the IMPACT tasks, teachers obtain valuable feedback both about children's performances on specific maths tasks and about the tasks themselves. Parents are able to alert the teacher to weaknesses and strengths and nothing about the child's performance in maths comes as a surprise at the end of the year or when statutory assessments are administered.

The diaries are a crucial part of this homework scheme.

Help with implementing IMPACT

Schools that wish to get IMPACT started by means of a series of staff meetings or in-service days may like to purchase the IMPACT INSET pack which contains everything that is needed for getting going. This is available from IMPACT Supplies Ltd, PO Box 1, Woodstock, Oxon OX20 1HB.

Useful telephone numbers

IMPACT Central Office (for information and assistance): 071 607 2789 at the University of North London on extension 6349. IMPACT Supplies Ltd (for diaries and INSET pack): 0993 812895.

Correlation of the Scottish maths curriculum with the English curriculum

The Scottish curriculum is divided into the Attainment Outcomes given below.

(PSE) Problem-solving and enquiry skills

(IH) Information handling

(NMM) Number, money and measurement

(SPM) Shape, position and movement

PSE is the equivalent of using and applying maths

IH permeates the Scottish maths curriculum, in that its requirements apply to all maths activities in NMM and SPM.

English subject	Scottish
Number	NMM
Money	NMM
Measuring	NMM
Number patterns	NMM
Shape and space	SPM
Data handling	IH

Correlation of the Northern Ireland maths curriculum with the English curriculum

The Northern Ireland curriculum is divided into the Attainment Targets (ATs) given below.

(AT N) Number

(AT A) Algebra

(AT M) Measures

(AT S) Shape and space

(AT D) Handling data

English subject	Northern Ireland
Number	AT N
Money	AT M
Measuring	AT M
Number patterns	AT A
Shape and space	AT S
Data handling	AT D